THE HIDDEN AFFAIR

THE STORY OF A FORMER FIRST LADY,
DETERMINED TO SHATTER THE SILENCE

GODZCHILD PUBLICATIONS

Published by Godzchild Publications
a division of Godzchild, Inc.
22 Halleck St., Newark, NJ 07104
www.godzchildproductions.net

Printed in the United States of America 2018 - 1st Edition
Cover Designed by Maurice Downing of MoDesignz
Back Cover Design and Formatting by Ana Esther of Es3lla Designs

Library of Congress Cataloging-in-Publications Data
The Hidden Affair: The Story of a Former First Lady, Determined
to Shatter the Silence/Dorothy Denise Hayes

ISBN   978-1-942705-51-2 (pbk.)
         978-1-942705-52-9 (hardcover)

1. Hayes, Dorothy Denise. 2. Truth 3. Women 4. Healing
5. Ministry 6. Christianity 7. Spiritual 8. Religion

2018

TABLE OF Contents

To God The Father, The Son, & The Holy Ghost. On April 27, 2017,
you woke me up with the vision to write my story, gave me the title, and told me
WHY this was necessary, and confirmed that I was indeed ready. I thank and
praise you for ALL THINGS! The pain, the tears, the betrayals…the list is
infinite.
You are My Absolute Everything!!!

This book is also dedicated to First Ladies of churches, countries, and households
around the world. Although I am aware that this story DOES NOT hold
true for all first ladies, I am saddened to discover that this is the heart of the
matter for many. I take this time to applaud those amazing husbands who have
undoubtedly stayed committed and remained faithful to their vows to God, and to
their beautiful wives. You are true Kings and I honor you all.

My heart bleeds for your truths, First Ladies, to come to light. You are NOT
just a first lady to your husband, but you are a woman who contains so much
more! God has ordained you, spoken destiny into you, and anointed you as well,
to be an instrument of His. You belong to God FIRST, then to your husbands.
I pray that this book will encourage you to soar, allow you to see a different
perspective, and even help many of you to completely heal and display your God-
given smile again. You absolutely deserve it! Be Blessed Beautiful Woman!

DISCLAIMER

I have tried to recreate events, locales and conversations from my memories of them. In order to maintain their anonymity in some instances I have changed the names of individuals and places, I may have changed some identifying characteristics and details such as physical properties, occupations and places of residence.

INTRODUCTION

A re you kidding me Lord? Why is it that you ask me to do some of the craziest things? I already know that people look at me as if I'm some type of holy-roller Looney-tune. Members have fallen off and I happen to believe that some of it may have to do with the WORD OF THE LORD you so frequently give to me. But really, Lord?

You want me to go to someone else's church for seven weeks and bring my entire congregation with me? You want me to attend two services every week, our worship service and theirs? I don't even know these people! But ok God...Fine! Yes! Of course I'll go! You already know I'll do whatever you say. And I know this is you because I've been hearing her name in the wind over the last two months. Never once have I heard of this woman, and now suddenly her name is dropped into my hearing over four times in two months? *Pastor Denise Baker.*

On a random Monday morning while dropping off my son at the Junior Police Academy's weeklong trip, all the parents and grandparents are saying their goodbyes. A very nice woman with a gorgeous mane of silver begins to tell me a doom's tale about her granddaughter. She is hoping and mainly praying that this program will be a beacon of light and turn her baby's mindset in the opposite direction. She says her Pastor, Denise Baker is a great example of a virtuous woman and desperately wishes that her grandbaby would be more like her.

Then there was the church service that I attended in Yonkers, NJ that had a flyer for the Women's Conference being held in August. Can you guess who the main speaker was going to be at this service? Yep, you guessed it! Pastor Denise Baker. At the moment, I cannot recall all the specifics of the other two occurrences, but these two instances were enough for me to submit to God and to shout, ALRIGHT!

Okay God, what are you saying to me concerning this woman? So, of course, when I got a prophecy to go to her church, I knew that this was you. Once again, like always in my life, you win God! I'll tell the church on Sunday, and prepare for possibly another resignation letter. God, you are something else."

This is how it all started. This is how I eventually met my now ex-husband, Dorian. Excuse me, *Pastor* Dorian O. Woodson. I must introduce him as 'Pastor' because anything less would be an insult and disrespectful to his existence. On one particular occasion I discovered, along with the rest of the world, that it was *Dr. Dorian O. Woodson.* Although a certificate or any other confirming documents to validate this title was never located or produced. While once airing on The Word Network, the name at the bottom of the screen read Dr. Dorian O. Woodson. "Ummmm, when did you become a Doctor?" I asked while viewing the snippet he texted me of his segment that was to air in about two weeks. He claims it was an honorary degree. "When did you receive this? And why are you using it now? If you have this title, why is it that no one has ever referred to you as such? YOU yourself have never answered to Dr. Anything, so why now? Is *public image* a thing with you?" Why oh why did I ever ask that question? He was obviously offended to say the least. "How dare you question my authenticity? I am a myriad of ideas you know nothing of. " (How correct he was with this statement) "We just met less than a year ago, so you could not possibly be aware of all that I embody, as well as all of my numerous accomplishments to date." Ok... but Dorian never directly answered the question. Something I regrettably would get accustomed to him doing pretty often, but never became comfortable with at all.

So why do we settle ladies? Why is it when the crimson colored flags are blowing in the winds at a speed of 95 mph, directly in front of our simple little faces, do we ignore The Holy

Spirit when He is warning us to PAY ATTENTION, GIRL!!!! It's not "Something told me" or "I had a gut feeling," it is The Holy Spirit himself leading you into all truths.

Perhaps it was because he was a Pastor. That should account for a lot right? He doesn't just attend church on a weekly basis, he leads the church and is responsible for spiritually guiding the lives of trusting individuals who believe God called him. Maybe it was because God had told me to prepare to become a wife again so this must be the one, yeah? Or maybe, just maybe, it was the demon that so many women host within ourselves; you know the one that is mentioned in Matthew 12:22: The blind and mute demon that prohibits individuals from *seeing* and *speaking*.

"I know he did not avoid my question again!" He usually has the memory of an elephant. To such a degree that he would quickly recount a childhood story of when the neighborhood children prohibited him from entering the community pool because he jokingly pretended to urinate in it. He ran home crying from the mistreatment and the rejection of his "so-called" friends and it still affects him to this very day. This story in particular was so vividly painted, and to the extent that I could now picture each and every evil child in my mind, and I wanted to cause them physical bodily harm for hurting him so deeply! But all of a sudden he conveniently couldn't remember anything now? He left over an hour ago to run to the corner store! "Where did he go? Where was he all of this time?" I wondered. "

How dare I question the Man-of-God?" Although this may not be your story, it is definitely mine. My eyes were wide open. I prayed; I fasted; I prayed fast... (*Some of you will catch that on the drive home from work.*) I thought I did everything right. So how did I end up here? How did I end up with my daddy's gun in my hand, loaded and locked on Dorian's face, and ready to end both of our lives?

Dorian was good; and *this* is an understatement on how to adequately describe his well-performed act. And the Oscar, the Golden Globe, the Emmy, and the Best New Actor in a Drama Series goes to....

He was such an incredibly fine actor that you could not pay me to believe he could do anything like this. I would never have believed *anyone* (not my momma or my BFF of 30+ years) if they were to tell me that he wasn't who I thought he was...Who we **ALL** thought he was...Only God himself could reveal this well kept secret to me. And oh how The Lord revealed. On that faithful day in question, I finally discovered why it all went so horribly wrong. Why every piece of the puzzle began to crumble, and yet now successfully come together all at the same time, and why my life as I knew it had completely fallen apart. This is the unimaginable day that I learned of my husband's HIDDEN AFFAIR.

> *For there is nothing hidden that will not be disclosed, and nothing concealed that will not be known or brought out into the open. - Luke 8:17 NIV*

CHAPTER

"THE BROKEN-HEARTED"

hat Becomes of the Brokenhearted? Sadness, bitterness, and sometimes DEATH!

The title of this 1966 hit by Jimmy Ruffin, is a question many wives in the church have asked themselves time and time again. Let me preface this statement by acknowledging my awareness that not only are wives in the church asking this question, but many other women, and men who have experienced this heartbreak want to know the answer as well. My focus, though, on our plight (first ladies and former first ladies) comes from a kaleidoscope of thoughts that have been seared into the minds and souls of the women who take this unspoken vow. To love, honor, obey and cover your husband's secret sins; to keep quiet and lift those hands up in praise, to squeamishly watch him lay unholy hands on the unsuspecting members of the congregation; to wave and smile while dying inside each and every Sunday morning. And as if that weren't enough, we are then reminded by other first ladies that our responsibilities as good Christian wives are to intercede in prayer for them, commit to spiritual warfare for your marriage, pray and fast for their breakthrough, all with the hopes that maybe one day he will repent and become all that God has called him to be. Well, what becomes of the brokenhearted when none of the above works?

Although considered a man's disease, statistics show that more women have died from cardiovascular disease than men. Did you happen to know that one form of heart disease is called *"Broken Heart Syndrome?"* Yes!!! Your heart can become so emotionally damaged and stressed that the grief leads to an actual broken heart. Many people have died from what is officially known as cardiomyopathy. This ailment may very well be the real issue which appears as a heart attack. This heart muscle disease is a progressive disease in which the heart is abnormally enlarged, thickened, and/or stiffened due to trauma and/or severe stress. As a result, the heart muscle's ability to pump blood is weakened, often causing heart failure. Now who would have thought that dying from a broken heart is as much a reality as succumbing to cancer, diabetes, or a stroke? A change in our thought processes must come.

Can you even imagine enduring this kind of heart-wrenching pain? The kind of unbearable and excruciating pain that would lead a human's heart to rebel against its natural course of action. Several mothers have experienced this during the loss of their child. Spouses have departed their lives early when their soul-mate's life was suddenly no more; and a ministry friend of mine, another first lady, was hospitalized for weeks after discovering that her husband, the pastor, was *yet again* entangled in another 'situation' at the church. After submitting to several tests and exams, the results concluded that she had a stressful heart condition, but the usual causes of such could not be found.

This particular event in question involved her husband having an affair with the head of the Liturgical Dance Ministry, which then resulted in *her* carrying *his* child. The rumor was that she was a few months pregnant and had just lost their baby. The Pastor, my friend's husband, refused to leave this woman's side for nearly two weeks straight. All under the pretenses that she was heavily grieving, speaking of suicide and the *Pastor* had to offer his unwavering support to ensure her mental, emotional, and spiritual stability. He was resistant to the idea of leaving her with family and friends regardless of them volunteering their availability, because he and only he could understand the depths of grief that a parent would have over the loss of a child. *Ummmm, Yeah ok…can somebody say Manipulation 101?*

Instead of my friend leaving her husband after several years, despite the revelatory information that she received about many 'other women', she decided to ignore it all. The sobering truth was that she knew it was not a lie. This was not his first, second, third, or even fourth indiscretion that she had to face. At this particular time, they had now been married for 18+ years and she had learned how to smile and wave as if she was a runner up in The Miss America Pageant. The sad thing about the runner-up is that you share the same amount of stage and space with the winner, but you never receive the crown.

I know I know, and I can see it now...all the many wives with their eyebrows raised and their necks swaying, fingers snapping... ready to clap back: "But he comes home to me every night!" or "At the end of the day, he is, and will always be mine." We also have the ladies who decide, "She can have him for a minute but he is mine for a lifetime", and of course the worst one—the lie that we have perpetuated in every young male child, and every woman who knows she should leave but her momma, aunties, and grandma-ma raised her to believe, "Girl calm down... A man will be a man". I can also hear the more refined, spiritual, and sophisticated responses of those first ladies who wave their tear-stained banner of commitment, loyalty, and boast in their wedding vows (especially the part that says "Until Death do us Part"). Okay beloved, I understand your position, and honestly respect your decision. Please just be aware and cautioned, my beautiful sister-friend, that it very well may be YOUR death on the account of YOUR overwhelmed heart, one day deciding that Enough is finally Enough.

> *The LORD is close to the brokenhearted and saves those who are crushed in spirit. - Psalms 34:18 NIV*

CHAPTER

"THE CONFERENCE"

During the "DUNAMIS...AND YOU SHALL RECEIVE POWER" Conference is when our lives and paths crossed. I had been cordially invited by Pastor Timothy Baker, Pastor Denise's husband, to partake in a weekend of empowerment sessions, pastoral leadership courses, and the witnessing of an elevation ceremony of pastors who had become new covenant partners with this up-and-coming mega church, Hope Church in New Jersey. Pastor T, as everyone affectionately calls him, was one of those new covenant partners. We had briefly met and were only familiar with one another via ministry so I was honored when I received the invitation. His wife, Pastor Denise Baker and I, on the other hand, had hit if off after meeting for the first time. Remember that church I mentioned earlier? You know, the one that God instructed me to attend with my congregation for seven weeks straight? Well, I did. And would you believe that this woman of God, Pastor Denise Baker, was waiting for ME?!! The Lord had already spoken to her instructing Pastor Denise to receive me as a confidant, and a few other ladies that would follow. God declared that he was sending women to her who would walk with her during a challenging season of her life. And this is why (just one of the reasons why) I love God! *Only* God could have set up such an encounter!

As everyone entered into the sanctuary for the evening service, excitement filled the atmosphere. I could hardly wait to get inside and get a good seat smack dab in the center of it all! I absolutely love the word of God, and the preacher for the evening was none other than the love child of Merriam-Webster and the New Oxford American Dictionaries, the always profound, sesquipedalian himself, Bishop Noel Jones. He could annihilate and reconstruct a passage of scripture like nobody's business, and I was certain that tonight would be no different. My BFF/ armor-bearer/everything-that-I-would-ever-need-to-get-done-in-a-lifetime-sister Joyce was with me. She is not impressed by most preachers but she loves Bishop Jones, even more than I do, so she was excited as well about the service. We are both extremely low key and prefer to get in and out of services. I come to hear a word from God, (and on this night, I also came to support a friend in the ministry), worship and praise my savior, then go home to bask in the glory. Just give me God and His glory; I give Him my worship and my offerings, and I am good!

As droves of people began to find their way through the sanctuary, the praise and worship team took the stage and then it all began. Lights…camera…action! Literally. Enormous stage lights descended from above in all shades and spectrums of a rainbow twisting and turning, while the camera crew quickly dashed up and down the aisles of this sacred space. Huge spotlights were fixated on the lead singers of the worship team, and any victim who happened to be in an aisle seat was almost always pushed in an effort for one of the cameramen to catch that perfect moment of worship from an unsuspecting child of God. The stage itself was impressive in décor and adornments, although the Buckingham Palace furniture could be a bit much. Almost center-stage, directly behind the choir was a free-flowing waterfall with the most beautiful array of colors you could have ever seen. Just then, at what seemed to be a moment meticulously timed to appear like a natural occurrence but was too obvious to pass *that* test, the worship leader belted out a high note while miraculously a hidden choir suddenly appeared. I thought to myself, "Is Jesus coming back tonight?" Then the moment of truth; the elite court of Pooh-Pas strolled down one of the main aisles escorted by the security paparazzi. I was like "Whoa! Where is Jay, Bey, Blue-Ivy and the twins??!!! They must be in the building for all of this to be going down!"

You may be asking yourself right now, "What in the world is a Pooh-Pa? My late Pastor, the great Evangelist Sheila Johnson had developed a term for the men and women of God who loved the adoration of men, needed the titles of the elite, and could not fathom living without hearing their names called over the pulpits of America. She affectionately knew these 'church folk' as the Pooh-Pa's.

Now please do not misunderstand my annoyance, but I humbly ask that you humor me and allow me to share my perspective. I wholeheartedly believe in progressive ministry. I believe creativity and artistry woven into ministry is a representation of God's perfect design. He is the Genesis of all creativity. According to Revelation 21, the walls of heaven are made of jasper, and the city itself is erected of actual pure gold; in fact, a gold so pure that the color of it appears as transparent as glass! The foundations of the city walls were decorated with every kind of precious stone from sapphires, to emeralds, rubies, jasper, and a few others that are difficult to pronounce. It's extremely necessary that I also mention the beautiful gates constructed of exquisite fine pearls and streets of pure, crystal clear gold. And, I most certainly am not referring to that yellow brick road that we've often watched and sang to and attempted to skip along with as young children affixed to our television screens. Whether you preferred Judy Garland or the Diana Ross version as your genre of choice concerning this classic, the Land of Oz cannot ever begin to compare to the exquisite dwellings of heaven's headquarters.

My issue, or should I rephrase this and say my question, is "Where do we draw the line in our Houses of Worship?" How much is *too* much? I have a fiery desire to be intimate with my savior, but I do not necessarily want to have my face plastered on the three big screens that hover over the audience for everyone to see my sincere, yet very ugly-cry face. Of course I understand the need for these screens in sanctuaries that are blessed to accommodate large groups of people. Even the bloody nose seats want to see the messenger delivering the word of God. But we have not gathered here together, well at least I am not there to see the audience and their personal reactions and responses towards God. We are there to listen to the person releasing the word of God, whether that is via singing, preaching, or prophesying. When I lay prostrate before the Lord or bow my knees to reverence Him, I would prefer *not* to see it pop up on one of my social media timelines with a hashtag stating, #AwesomeWorshipService.

Well, I digress. The actual service, once the antics ceased and the word of the Lord was preached, was really very good. Immediately after, Joyce and I quickly gathered up our belongings and headed towards the back of the sanctuary. We had high hopes of avoiding the long lines of awaiting cars trying to be first in regards to getting out of this massive parking lot. Our get-away plan was suddenly foiled as Pastor Denise excitedly ran over to us. She was accompanied by a few friends in the ministry, and wanted us all to meet one another. She began the introductions of her friends, mainly pastors, but this last friend of hers garnered a longer more thought-out mini bio. They were long time friends, and in their younger years, they did the church scene together as teens and young adults. A group of them would conduct prayer meetings in their parent's basements, form musical groups, and basically participated in all things God.

Now because Pastor Denise and I had been spending a lot of time together, getting to know one another and attempting to discover why God Himself had decided to create this divine union, she now knew that I was single. She often joked that one of her goals was to find me a nice, handsome, and saved man. Not that I needed any type of help in that department. I was very happy, content, and just plain ole good living with my single self, and my main goal was to remain about my Father's business. Regardless of my stance, Pastor Denise had something different in mind. The gentleman that garnered the final and most lengthy introduction was her longtime friend, Pastor Dorian Woodson. He pastored a church in the Bronx and appeared to be extremely uptight and rigid. Pastor Dorian didn't smile at all. In truth he appeared to be aloof and preoccupied. We quickly shared hellos and handshakes, and that was enough for me. "Nice meeting everyone, and have a good night," I stated as Joyce and I headed out of the sanctuary. Pastor Denise caught up to us just as giddy as she could be. "Soooooo, what do you think?" she asked.

"About what?" I asked.

She said, "Are you serious? About Pastor Dorian? What do you think?!"

"Wait a minute, you introduced me to him to try and hook me up? Stop it! He's not my type."

Pastor Dorian just seemed way too serious and overly formal for me. In stature he stood about 5'9 and was also very slim. I'm a thick chic and...yeah, just a no for me, not my type at all. Joyce quickly backed me up by saying, "Yes, definitely not her type."

"See that's the problem. Ya'll have too many types. He needs to be this; he has to look like that. God is probably trying to send you somebody but he may not come in the package that you're looking for," she so sweetly snapped back.

"He's a really nice guy, DeeDee. Well he'll be here all weekend for the conference. I think he's nice so you should think about it," she suggested.

"Think about what?" I wondered. I did not come here for that, and I'm good, seriously. I think everywhere we go together is an opportunity for Pastor Denise to 'introduce me' to someone she knows. Honestly, I really thought nothing of it.

Pastor Denise left us to our bff conversation. Joyce, who is always vocal concerning her perspective, whether asked or not said, "Did she really think she was going to hook you up with *him*?"

I said, "I know!! He is whack! All serious and corny; "Hello Pastor DeeDee" in his super-tense and stuffy Pooh-Pa voice.

"Man listen... No swag, no confidence, no nothing but that tan suit and his tan teeth. Did you see his teeth?!!" I laughingly asked Joyce.

"You know I saw his teeth and you know me...I don't do yellow teeth!" I reassured her. As if she didn't know me better than anyone on this earth.

I'm sorry, Lord. I am not vain but I like what I like and nice, white teeth is something that I do like. If I'm wrong Lord, then deliver me from the desire of a man with pearly whites. Your word says there are pearly gates in heaven, and I prefer that the gate of a man's mouth be of the same substance. Besides the teeth, I am way too free, spontaneous and outgoing for him. He could stand to loosen up a bit and relax, but wait; who am I? I am not here to size anyone up and I'm sure he did not come here to meet my standards. I did not decide to attend this conference to meet anyone; point blank period. I came to support Pastor T on his installation, and to hear the Word of The Lord for my life. That is it, and that is all. Obviously, Pastor Denise had other plans.

The morning after seemed promising and I was excited to

learn of the agenda for the day. Just a sidebar, I LOVE to learn! I believe that we should learn something new each and everyday of our lives. You could discover how to write a dissertation, or something simpler as learning how the addition of a little salt will enhance the flavor and creaminess of coffee (without the added fat).

The pastors and leaders were to be separated today and had to attend separate classes so that meant that the bff and I were going to be parting ways today like the Red Sea. Coolbeans, and absolutely no worries for me. Unlike my home-girl Joyce, I am always open to meeting new people, sometimes against my better judgment. And again, I came to learn and grow spiritually, as well as intellectually.

As I was headed to the first session of the day I ran into Pastor T outside of the classroom in the hallway. We came in and sat together while the session had just begun. What would you know? Pastor Dorian was teaching this class. As I was emptying my briefcase of notebooks, pens, and highlighters I was impressed by the information presented and the caliber of vocabulary utilized by Mr. Dorian. "Okay...I see you." What happened next was refreshingly breathtaking. He began to share a very personal story about events from his past that were very devastating and traumatic. As I began to cry, Pastor T handed me some tissue and gently consoled me. Pastor Dorian spoke about finding liberty in exposing our truths because he happens to deeply believe everything in the word of God. We overcome by the blood of the lamb, and the testimony of the saints (Revelation 12:11). While teaching and giving some of his personal testimony, Pastor Dorian expressed himself with laughter and silly jokes. He smiled and engaged us with overt gestures, reenactments of his past, and I found myself noticing a slight bit of swag. Do you guys remember the scene in the movie *Boomerang* when Eddie Murphy would see a fine woman while being out and about? He would shift his head to the right and see the objects in view quite differently. His face exuded a look of pleasant confusion. The look said, 'Ummmm, I think I am interested in what I am gazing upon." Well that was my thought process at this very moment. *Maybe there is more to this guy than meets the initial eye.*

During our session, Pastor Denise came in and spotted us in class. She had slept in that morning and was now vibrant and revived. She made her way over to us and sat down next to me. She leaned over and said, "Oh look at God. Look who's teaching this first class?!" I just laughed and looked at her as if to say, "Whatever sis." When the class was dismissed Pastor Denise and I checked out our schedule to decide where we would go next. After trekking up a few flights of stairs to the second floor of this grand facility, we were almost run down by guess who? Pastor Dorian. He was a totally different man than the previous night.

What a difference a day makes. He charmingly joked that he left the brothers behind and he decided to follow the ladies and allow us to direct him to the next session. He did offer a suggestion that we go to his friend's session, Pastor Reagan Hubbins' class. He was one of the many pastors teaching sessions this weekend. We conceded and indeed the course was powerful and insightful. Today was turning out to be a very good day.

I texted Joyce so we could catch up because it was now time for lunch. We met in the fellowship hall and sat down at the table with the Bakers and their friends. Pastor Denise tried to finagle the seating so that I ended up next to Pastor Dorian, at another table, but I saw it coming so Joyce and I casually sat two tables over. When our table was motioned to go up and get our food, I walked towards the buffet area and saw from my peripheral vision on the left that Pastor Dorian quickly jolted up from his table that was *not* called and sidelined his way up front, and landed directly behind me in the line. He commented on the extra onions that I requested from the server to add to my already oniony fish selection. He questionably quipped, "Do you know what all of that is going to do to your breath?"

"I most certainly do, and this is why I always have gum and mints in my purse. I love onions and garlic and will continue to eat them whether alone or in the company of my peers," I smiled and boldly stated back.

He said he was impressed. "So, you're really not concerned about all this going on around you are you?" he asked.

I am assuming that he was referring to the fact that Pastor Mark Chironna had just entered the room, and there were many other well known people of God who had flown in to attend today's afternoon session. The buzz and excitement was all over their faces and most were discreetly crowding around them waiting for introductions and picture opportunities. "No not really," I responded. " I am hungry and this fish looks amazing."

We engaged in some small talk about the content of his class. I shared with him how moved I was by his transparency and his testimony of endurance. He said he initially wasn't going to share it and after reviewing it again in his head, had no intentions of doing so, but the spirit unctioned him and he went forth. The line had quickly come to an end so we parted ways. I walked back to my table and he returned to his.

Shorty after, Pastor Dorian came over and told me that he was leaving early to return to New York and asked if he could exchange numbers for ministry purposes. "Ministry purposes? Okay, right." I thought. "No problem" I answered as I gave him my business card. Suddenly his eyes lit up. "You're an independent distributor with OG? So am I!" he said excitedly. "Wow, what a coincidence. It was really nice meeting you. Enjoy the rest of the conference."

Now here comes Pastor Denise. "Did I see you give him your card?" she asked. "Yes ma'am, for ministry purposes only. You were right though; he seems like a nice guy. But like I said, I'm good and he's ok. Not out here searching for anything," I responded.

I decided to finish my lunch and get my head together for Pastor Chironna. That man is brilliant! I didn't want to miss a thing during his session. As Joyce and I walked into the sanctuary to secure our seats, Pastor Denise came over and began to smile. "I have a good feeling about this DeeDee." She smiled with that infectious smile and then went to find a seat next to her husband.

"She is funny," I said to Joyce.

Joyce replied, "Yes she is. And I saw you give him your card too… ummmm. Now he did seem much better today than he was last night, but remember this; he still has yellow teeth."

I just hollered!!! "I can not with you Joyce!" I laughed.

"I'm just saying, I'm just reminding you of what you said you don't like. You are always the one to compromise," she reminded me.

I didn't give it much thought because remember, I did not come here for all of that. After we composed ourselves from hysterically laughing, we prepared to receive the impartation that was surely to come. Mark Chironna is going to be good! I can feel it in my spirit! Let's go God!

> *Many are the plans in the mind of a man, but it is the purpose of the Lord that will stand.* —Proverbs 19:21 ESV

CHAPTER

"MY MARRIAGE MENTALITY"

The idea of marriage did not consume me; not like it appears to overwhelm many of the women I know. Statistics reveal that although the number of legal marriages in the United is decreasing, 2600 college aged women expressed that they would like to be married by the age of 30. According to a survey conducted by HerCampus.com, 85.1 percent said that they'd like to be married by age 30. Specifically, 46.5 percent said they'd like to get married between age 25 and 27; 20.9 percent said they'd like to tie the knot between 28-30; and 17.1 percent want to walk down the aisle by their 25th birthday. Twenty-five years old? Are you kidding me? It is difficult to believe that we can correctly fathom the complete and fullness of who we are in our twenties. The even more depressing reality is that the majority of us will never discover who we were formed and shaped to become simply because we do not want to do the work. Growth is constant, and when we assume that we have reached our pinnacle beings, matured completely, and have completed our process, then we indeed deceive ourselves and ultimately stunt our growth.

The Lord had been telling me to prepare, again, for marriage. But my thought process was just like this…*well, you know God…I don't quite think… after some thought…I think I'm okay. Yeah, God I took some time to think and reflect and ummm…#IssaNoGod!!!!*

See I was never the kind of woman who *had* to be married. It was never a major goal for my life, not like it was for so many of my girlfriends. A few of my girlfriends would collect bridal magazines and dream in full living color of the day when they would become the star of the show in that beautifully flowing glamorous white gown (knowing that the more appropriate color of choice for us should've been tan). Some of the women I knew even attended bridal shows and events to get a head start for the actual day, although no actual concrete relationship was ever in sight. And the saddest events to date were when a few of them would attempt to make *every* guy they dated "The One." I never completely understood the desperation and wildly creative plans implemented to secure that ring and that infamous walk down the aisle. I don't know; it just wasn't on my top ten to-do list. Now of course I figured that I would one day get married because my thought process was that a husband and children just came with the package called 'Adulthood.' My main focus was how to make money, and then make more of it.

I will admit, I played with Barbie dolls like most young girls, but my Barbie had a pink corvette and a big house. My Barbie-doll couldn't throw down in the kitchen like Rachel Ray, but her main concern was *not* if Ken came over for dinner or not. She would be a global world traveler, become the next discovered famous entertainer, and make boatloads of money doing it! My Barbie would allow her hair to blow in the wind as she put that baby corvette in reverse, sped out of her 3-car garage with the top down, and flew down the highway all while bumping her Diana Ross!!! She had places to go and people to see. Now Ken could come if he wanted to, but if not...hasta la Vista Baby!! Whoo-hoo!!

I believe in love and actually now, I am in love with the idea of marriage, established God's way, but so far, holy matrimony has not worked in my favor. I had already been married, twice, and I did not do a great job with the selection of my former spouses. Both of my ex-husbands committed adultery, which in turn severely compromised the marital bonds we once shared.

My first marriage basically happened because I was pregnant and he was my "baby daddy." Never ever allow this to be the reason why you decide to marry, ladies or gentlemen! We had spoken of marriage throughout our three-year relationship, but because we were often on-again and off-again, I did not put too much weight on those conversations; at least not until the positive plus sign appeared on the three *different* pregnancy tests I had taken that morning. Again, and I stress, never marry because of an unplanned pregnancy. I was 22 years old and had just graduated from Kean University. Although I was an adult, I was raised in the church and did not want to become that girl; the knocked up one, living in sin with no husband in sight.

My momma would indirectly tell my sister and I, via the numerous phone conversations she had with her sisters, "DeeDee and Karin know they better not ever come up in this house pregnant!" So because I was still living in *that* house, I was terrified! What would she say? Where was I going to live? I knew she would let me stay, but I wouldn't feel comfortable with those arrangements. This was my responsibility, not hers. Mommy had already done her part by raising two beautiful children as a single parent, and my child was mine to do the same. Surprisingly, she was elated when I told her that I was expecting. I had received some news in my late teens that it would be a 'challenge' for me to conceive naturally, so she was actually relieved that her daughter would experience motherhood. However, I was raised in a household where I only saw my dad on weekends and I did not desire that life for my child. Not to mention, I still felt the pressures from some within my church environment, and the convictions in my heart to get married. When my child's father reminded me that he had already wanted to marry me before the pregnancy, I consented and said yes. He was not a man of God, and I definitely was a far cry from the woman I am today. A church group sponsored cruise was how we met, but the church and the God that we heard about on Sunday mornings, was not within us.

Our parents were active for years in the church so I thought the history of God within our upbringing and lineage was enough God for us, too. I have never been more wrong. We had not been married for more than a year before he began to cheat. Not only did he begin to cheat, he had also become verbally and physically abusive. Now I need you to understand some of the lessons I've learned from my mommy. My mother, the same woman I was and still am afraid of to this day, didn't raise any punks. We were taught to be respectful and to never start a fight, but if one was started with us, we had better finish it! This type of parental guidance may seem a bit harsh to some, but my momma had to fight throughout her childhood on many occasions, and then had to fight off my daddy for ten years. I thoroughly understood her reaction to physical aggression, and why she taught the lessons she did with her babies. She taught two young girls many things about life, and a few of those lessons included "uppercuts and jabs" just in case.

I loved to watch and learn techniques from the mighty moves of Mike Tyson, so it's safe to say that I was not the lady who would just sit there and take a fight laying down. (And to think, I was the calm one in our family of three feisty women). I was a lover and not a fighter; well at least I didn't think so, until I was pushed... literally.

Although I did not resort to fighting as a first response to an argument, it had become the norm in our household. I knew that this was not the example that I desired to model in front of our son. At the time I could not understand how I married my father when I despised what he did to my mom. I refused to raise another abuser so I decided to leave. However, I did not leave immediately. My marital vows were something that I did not take lightly so we attempted again to work on our marriage, but after my trusty and expensive private investigator solidified my women's intuitions, I had had enough. *I have to fight you, and share you? Nah bro. I'll take singleness for $1,000 Alex.* While reflecting on everything that happened in this marriage I often thought to myself, "Did I do everything to save the marriage?" I recalled a lengthy counseling session with our Pastor at the time. I was 'encouraged' to forgive like the Bible declares and to work on the marriage. Although our Pastor was adamant about physical abuse being unacceptable, he also was *extremely lenient* regarding the violations of the marital covenant of fidelity being broken. Why is that?

Please, learn from my lessons and unwise decisions. If there is a lack of self-control from either of you then marriage should not be considered. Marriage will require you to control your mouth, your emotions, your anger, your temper, your eyes, your need to control others, and everything in between.... *Come on somebody!!!*

My second marriage occurred after I had given my life to the Lord and refused to live in sin. There is a difference between going to church, and living for God. I chose to do the latter. We had already been dating, which equated to sex. In an average relationship, sex is a given. It's sad to say but I am not just referring to the unchurched. We had already been sleeping together for over a year and I knew once I cut it off, he would go elsewhere to fulfill his needs. Remember, he was not a man of God, and I had just begun my walk with God. So I ended the relationship and walked away. He followed me with a proposal and a sizable diamond ring in hand. I used the same scripture that many other hot and heavy Christians give in our time of need: "But if they cannot control themselves, they should marry, for it is better to marry than to burn with passion." (1Corinthians 7:9 NIV) Passion, love, and commitment are all different.

I often ponder the thought, "Do we truly comprehend the deep levels of pain infidelity can cause?" The mental and emotional trauma alone can have debilitating effects on the human psyche. Many women are prone to believe that men, as a majority, are insensitive to this reality, which in turn allows them to function in an adulterous lifestyle with no serious regard to our feelings. But I beg to differ. I believe men are just as damaged, if not more, when the reality of infidelity vis-a-vis their wives or significant others hits their homes. Several women have this superhuman, innate strength that allows us to pull from the depths of our innermost being to forgive these deplorable offenses; many times *reoccurring* offenses over a period of time. Men, on the other hand fight, struggle, and wrestle with the idea of forgiving such an offense. As we know, men are immensely visual creatures. The idea and reality of their woman giving herself to another man continuously replays in their minds. They often imagine the intense intimate moments you two share and visualize another man taking their place during such a sacred act. It can all be too much for the male ego to handle. More times than not, most men, even the saved ones, resolve that the betrayal cannot be forgiven and they make the decision to move forward in life without you. There remains a myriad of other dynamics that are involved in our decisions to fight or flee, such as self-esteem, self-value; culture, upbringing, socio-economic status, and the list can go on and on. Several books are written on this topic and this is *not* one of them, however, I do want to shine a light on one last observation: God himself **hates** divorce (Malachi 2:16 KJV)-the undoing of covenant promises between husbands and wives—yet He makes an allowance, not a mandate, for such to occur when adultery has entered into a marriage. -Selah

> *But a man who commits adultery has no sense; whoever does so destroys himself. —Proverbs 6:32 NIV*

CHAPTER FOUR

"DESSERT"

I met a host of other pastors and leaders at the Dunamis Conference. After we left the conference that day, I had a business meeting in Jersey City with some of my MLM partners, so needless to say, Joyce and I were extremely tired. After another successful session had ended, we got in the car and plopped down in the heated seats to take a breath before we got back on the road to head home. Since I turned my ringer off during the meeting, I was not aware of the messages that I had received during the last few hours. As I checked my messages, there were several numbers that I did not recognize, and these voicemails were all from earlier that evening. I asked Joyce to push play on my phone because I wanted to lay back and close my eyes for just a minute. Message one- "Hello Pastor DeeDee, this is Pastor Woodson from the conference this weekend. It was indeed a pleasure to have met you. I am going to be in New Jersey tomorrow at my friend's church on Chancellor Street, and I, ummmm, wanted to know if you would join me for dessert tomorrow evening after the service? Please give me a call, or you can text to let me know. Have a beautiful evening."

Midway through the message, I quickly sat my chair back up to the upright position and looked at Joyce with a look of complete perplexity.

"Do you hear his voice?! Who was that again? That's the pastor from today?" "Jesus! He sounds like Billy D. Williams!" I screeched.

"No he did not call my phone sounding like *that!!!* Do you remember him having such a velvety voice yesterday? My Lord. Replay that message," I demanded.

Joyce stared at me and raised that infamous right eyebrow that she often raises when she is both questioning the situation, and silently suggesting that I calm it all the way down. 'The eyebrow' usually signifies her possible disapproval and hesitation regarding the situation at hand. Oh how many times throughout the past thirty plus years have I experienced this quite amusing 'slow-ya-roll' gesture that only Joyce can give me. "Okay," she cautiously grinned.

Dessert. Now that was different! This was not a dinner invitation, which would normally imply that you most definitely want to get to know me, and most likely, that you are looking for something. And the invite wasn't for lunch which says I think I may be interested in you, but I need to see you in direct light again before I make up my mind that I'm attracted to you. Dessert. Who requests a meeting over dessert? I think I like that. It's unique and not the usual or common line to suggest that an additional encounter is desired. Dessert. It's flirty and confident. I think I like the idea of dessert. "I don't know Joyce. I promise that I am not interested in him or anyone for that matter. I like this chill-mode season God has me in, and besides, my focus needs to be on the church. I am not in the mood to date anyone right now," I bantered.

"Who said you were going to date him? The man just asked for dessert! But wow dude! He just met you yesterday and is already asking you out! He isn't wasting any time now is he?! He does have a nice voice though." She said.

"I know right?! And you are absolutely right. It's just dessert and besides, my eat-whatever-I-want-day is tomorrow soooo, what the heck? Why not go? It's only dessert." I said it as if I was attempting to not only convince Joyce, but myself as well.

Sunday morning service was on fire!!! We have this saying in our church, well after church service is over and we are now attempting to recollect ourselves from what God just did— "Were you in church today?!" we would often text, and then call one another to ask as if we did not know the answer. It was understood that asking this rhetorical question was necessary because the desire to continually express how awesome our God is, was overwhelming in our souls. Needless to say, we had one of these types of encounters that day. Now what was amazing is that we had not just one lit service, but two services today! But in the excitement of the day, I then realized that I was supposed to meet up with Pastor Dorian.

I had already replied, "Hello Pastor Dorian, dessert would be fine," via text, to Pastor Dorian's invitation. I gave him the location to a diner in Maplewood that I often frequent. We agreed on a 7pm meeting time, but because of our church anniversary service lasting longer than expected, I was now running late. By the way, I hate to arrive late to anything. I also have a major issue with our cultural acceptance of this irritating behavior that the majority of us consider a norm. I digress, my apology.

"Oh Jesus… it's cold out here!" I said shivering while walking to the car after our "turnt up" church anniversary service. I would absolutely hate the month of January had I not celebrated my own entrance into the world on the 24th of this artic and harshly frigid month. "Why did I agree to dessert? And why tonight!? You know it's colder outside at night time Joyce!" I fussed while riding up Springfield Avenue and admiring the remaining Christmas décor on the street light poles.

"You were impressed by that Billy D. Williams voice

remember," Joyce giggled.

"You right, you right," I joked. "Remember to call me as soon as you are ready to leave," she said.

"Yes ma'am, I will," I replied.

I notified Pastor Dorian of my arrival as Joyce and I pulled up outside of the dinner. Pastor Dorian had offered to pick me up from our church, but I declined. I never meet anyone without Joyce knowing my whereabouts. There are far too many unstable people out here, and my prayer life doesn't end when I leave the sanctuary; It actually increases…as it should. Since she had picked me up for church this morning it made sense for her to drop me off at the diner, instead of me having to go all the way back home to get my car. Joyce waved her goodbyes from inside of the car, and made a point of yelling out to me, and into his hearing, "Call me when you're done and I'll be out here ready and waiting!"

Although he had already secured a quaint little booth in the corner, Pastor Dorian met me at the entrance of the diner and held the door open as I asked to be excused for my lateness. He was more than willing to forgive the offense. As I was unbuttoning my burly winter coat, I noticed from my peripheral view that he had not yet sat back down. He was patiently standing, awaiting for me to reach the last button on my coat so that he could remove my coat from behind, neatly fold it into an almost perfect square, sit it next to *him* so that it wouldn't obstruct my seating area, and only proceeded to sit as he watched me take my seat first. *"Well okay then!"* I thought. This is not something I was accustomed to so needless to say, I was pleasantly thrown off guard. Now before I proceed with the story please give me some credit. It is not as if I've only dated thugs and derelicts. I am accustomed to doors being held open and chairs oftentimes being pulled out, but I would soon learn that Pastor Dorian was the walking epitome of the term 'The Perfect Gentleman.'

What I anticipated to be a nice, cordial conversation over dessert enveloped into a journey of shared memories that lasted until the patient waitress playfully whispered to us that the establishment was now closed. I believe we hit about every topic imaginable from business endeavors, to raising children; ministry highs and lows, and even shared a few horror stories from our previously failed marriages.

The vivid recollections and traumatic stories of his ex-wife were enough to depress even Mary Poppins!!! According to Dorian, nothing could make her happy, and it appeared to him that her one true purpose and goal in life was to agitate his simple existence. Cantankerous, spiteful, negligent, disrespectful, and selfish were only a handful of adjectives used to describe her persona. Despite seeking counsel over eight different occasions throughout their marriage, and despite his begging for help from the church bishops and pastors, nothing could change her, or save their 21 year-old marriage. He tried everything to make it work and when all had failed, he poured all of his time, love and attention into their two children as a solace and reprieve from his depressing marriage. As he so eloquently raked her through the coals, I was reminded of what my late pastor would always say; there are three sides to every story; his side, her side, and the truth. I eventually sought to hear her side of the story, but she refused to meet with me. Actually, she repudiated any invitations to meet me at all. I saw the email response to a request for dinner and conversation made by Dorian on my behalf. Let's just say her return email solidified that everything stated about her was the absolute truth.

He was adamant about our need to highlight and share our character strengths with one another. He spoke of his love for words and acquiring knowledge in diverse areas of study. I also learned that he was his mother's only caretaker and had moved her into his home to ensure that she received exceptional care. Although he had three other siblings, her medical and physical needs were his responsibility alone. His stance was that although he did not have help, he would ensure that his mother had everything she wanted and needed. *"This guy sounds like a modern day saint,"* I thought to myself. After we discussed the "good sides of us" I wanted to address the not-so-good traits that we bear. Of course, we could sit here all night and put our best foot forward, but I am a firm believer that a good pedicure can make even the ugliest feet more attractive. My desire was to address the weaknesses that definitely exist in all of us. Every single being on this planet is a constant work-in-progress. The problem exists when we actually believe we have completed our work. The greatest of us only thrive with constant renewal of our minds, persistently pushing towards being the best human we can possibly be, and understanding that even then, we are mere individuals who can only truly transform with a higher power. I am also a very transparent soul and firmly believe in exposing myself before the enemy can even think of using any of my past experiences against me. I call this Freedom!

But ask me how two people of God boldly went where no saved man or woman of God should go on their initial meeting? Because remember, this is not a date; it's just dessert. The topic of sexual appetites and preferences was presented. How did we get here? I felt the questioning on this subject was inappropriate for us to discuss at such an early stage in the game. Although I am an open book for the most part, I still felt that this topic, right now, was pushing it. What is he thinking? Pastor Dorian's response to the obvious look of concern on my face was, "We are both grown and intelligent people. Having this discussion is not only relevant to the flow of our conversation, but it also is revelatory. Why not lay it all on the table now? This way after tonight, we can decide if there will be another date/not date. We had discussed everything else, and mature folks can handle any conversation so it's really not a big deal correct?" (in case you didn't catch it, like I didn't at the time, that was manipulation. We'll discuss more of this topic later.)

Pastor Dorian stated that he decided before he left that Billy Dee voicemail that if I accepted his invitation for dessert, he was resolved to present his pure, truthful, unashamed, authentic self. No holds barred. He was at an age, 49, where there was no more time for being a false representation of himself. (I would soon discover that this too was a statement worthy of an Academy Award for Best Actor in a Drama Series.)

Pastor Dorian eloquently gave his perspective and synopsis concerning his experience with the previous women in his life. They were all crazy! In fact, "Most women are crazy," he stated. "Really, we are?" I asked with my version of Joyce's raised eyebrow. "Then please tell me why, if this is your absolute resolve, this invitation for dessert? Since most of us are crazy," I quickly responded.

"Well I was deeply engaged and smitten by your aura and your ease of conversation during our short meeting at the conference." He replied. "Your infectious demeanor and laughter is refreshing," he smiled. He mostly certainly has a way with words. Something he prides himself on.

Pastor Dorian began to speak of his recent resolve and conversation with God. No longer was God on the hook for sending him the love of his life. He, God, did not have to give him anyone else, and Dorian made the decision to forgo any additional prayer request for the woman he desired. Dorian was no longer going to be on the lookout for anyone. Actually, while preparing to teach a class at the conference, Pastor Dorian acknowledged that he was done with waiting for the One. He was content with serving God and pastoring his congregation as a single man. Although he professed to be a hopeless romantic, after the last 25 years of searching, he had finally decided that enough is enough. "All women are Crazy!" he concluded. I'll be okay on my own.

And then something remarkable happened. On that Friday evening, the night that must have been God-ordained; Dorian met Dee-Dee. He had now decided, after much deliberation, that he needed to know if this was truly God's intervention. She was quite different; distinctive from any other woman he had ever been with in the past. "And to think, just when I relinquished my dreams and desires over to God, my prayers have finally been answered," he secretly hoped and prayed. There was only one way to find out… Pursue her!

> *Desire without knowledge is not good, and whoever makes haste with his feet misses his way. —Proverbs 19:2 ESV*

CHAPTER

"WARNING...THE COUNTERFEITS ARE COMING!"

And pursue her he did. Pastor Dorian was positively incredible! Who was this guy? This has got to be too good to be true. "Dee-Dee, this can not be real! He is too good to be true" is what I often said concerning this man. Pastor Dorian arrived on the scene at a very pivotal time in my life. It was a nerve-wrecking season! One in which the Lord had been constantly warning me to beware of the counterfeits.

The definition of a counterfeit, according to Merriam-Webster is as follows: *made in imitation of something else with intent to deceive.*

Every other day, I would be reminded of the necessity to pay close attention to everyone in my life and to stay on my watch. I would read an article and the topic would somehow shift to the topic of a something or even someone being a counterfeit. I could watch a program on television, like a cooking show, and the host would state, "Make sure you use real cheese in this recipe, none of that counterfeit stuff." I was like wow! If this isn't you then I don't know what is Lord.

Sidebar, I love when God speaks to me like this!! He is an awesome God and He can not be denied! If you are not hearing and seeing God in these types of ways, ask Him to come into your life and blow your mind, like he is regularly blowing mine.

Okay Lord, I got it. So needless to say God was speaking, and speaking loudly, "But God, are you serious? You're warning me about falling for a counterfeit right now?" I curiously asked. This should be easy to spot, especially given the fact that there was no man in my life at the time, and I was not looking, praying, nor wishing for one. I am a very driven woman and although I love the idea of love, it is not nor has ever been my primary focus in life.

I also need to inform you that this same awesome God had been speaking to me about marriage, for about the last two years of my life. He would say I'm preparing you to be a Godly wife, and I would retort, *"Okay, but I'm good right now Lord."* I sincerely long to stay laser-focused on my personal development, handling the responsibilities of ministry, functioning adequately as a pastor, and getting my coins up. This sister will secure her own bag! For those who may not work with teenagers on a frequent basis, this phrase translates to mean that my financial future is in my hands and I am responsible for attaining and securing my own healthy bank accounts and portfolios.

So back to this counterfeit message, or warning, or whatever you want to categorize it as. I just continued to get them all of the time, and now I was actually nervous! I told my girls what the Lord had been warning me about and we were all on the lookout. Needless to say, men and their propositions began to come out of the woodwork! It is not uncommon to get a few double takes while at the mall, or a second glance while at the grocery store. We all experience that right? But what was occurring right now was quite interesting. Let's begin with suspect Number One.

His name was Charles, but he goes by Cee. Cee always wore a bandana on his head and he was an attractive man with a very nice smile. We've been at the same gym for years and always greet each other with a smile and a "Hey." Nothing more than that until today. Well, wait a second… He did make an attempt to get my number maybe about six years ago, but at that time I was married. He respectfully kept his distance and again, we would just greet each other whenever our paths crossed.

I have to believe that one day Cee noticed that I was no longer wearing my wedding ring. I was hitting the free weights and when done, I took off my training gloves. He would always workout with his boys and one morning he came over to help me re-rack the numerous weights I had sprawled out on the gym floor.

We had some small talk and then he told me about this big cookout that he hosts every year. He asked me to let all of my girlfriends know about the event which was in 3 weeks. He said I was invited too if my husband didn't have an issue with me hanging out with my girls for the day. *Now y'all know he was fishing right?* I was tempted to mess with him and give him no choice but to ask me, but I just stated that I was no longer married. With almost a child-like grin he replied, "Oh really? Would it now be possible for us to finally exchange phone numbers?"

I instantly replied, "Wow, you've been waiting all this time? It would be very possible for you to give me your number and for me to call you."

I explained that I do not allow just anyone to have my number, but we could talk a bit more while seeing each other at the gym. He laughed and said, "I could tell you are a woman with standards. No problem at all," he smiled and put his number into my phone.

I normally worked out from 5am to 6am because I needed to report to work by 7:30am. Now that the summer was here and I was off from work, I went to the gym later in the morning, between 10am and 11am. This is the reason I would run into Cee now. He was with the late morning gym crowd. I assumed he worked nights and went in after work.

Cee and I would meet up and talk between and mostly after working out. He and his friends seemed like cool dudes and I eventually gave him my number. Our conversations were light and casual. I didn't ask anything pressing or too personal because remember; I am watching out for the counterfeit. I did discover that he was an older guy with no children, and had recently sold his controlling shares in his company. He was very interested in me and would often tell me how pretty he thought I was. "Okay," I thought, that's nice, but I'm watching you, my friend. One topic of conversation (which was often discussed) was that of this annual cookout. Cee would light up and go on and on when sharing recollections of previous years, and he would give me the details on the mandatory prepping that was currently taking place for next Saturday. The selecting, purchasing, and seasoning of the meats and seafood in advance were under way. There was also the spraying down of the property this coming Thursday and Friday to ensure the elimination of mosquitos. See, this was impressive! *I hate mosquitos but they love them some Me!* Cee had to ensure the timely delivery and setup of the rented tables and chairs, and of course this magnificent occasion would not be complete without the deejay of the hour! "A deejay for a cookout at your house? Well shoot! What company did he own? Where does this guy live, and what does he do for a living that he has rented equipment and deejays for a cookout?" I wondered. A great playlist and portable speakers usually work fine me. Preparation of the grounds, top choice food, music spinning all night on the one's and two's...Well alright! *This sounds like this is going to be Thee Cookout of the Year!*

The Saturday had finally come for the big cookout, and I was excited! I did not invite all my girls because I was not in the mood for 21 questions about him; it was nothing serious between us, and I just didn't have the time for that. Now you know my home-girl Joyce was going to be there, and we had already decided to meet up at her house since she lived in Newark, too. I re-sent the text from Cee, giving me the address for Saturday, and I sent it to Joyce. She said the address was only about five minutes from her house, so we would leave about an hour after the cookout was to start. I initially thought nothing of it, but while driving to Joyce's house I was starting to trip out in my head. This man described this cookout as such a grand scale event that I visualized a huge backyard that was large enough to host at least two hundred people. There are several huge properties in Newark NJ, so after listening to his plans for the day, my thought process in regards to his home was not unreasonable. But these particular homes that I know of were not located in this bureau of Newark, so now I'm thinking "Wait a minute, where am I going? Well maybe it's off in the cut or somewhere that I don't know about," I thought.

I get to Joyce's house and when she gets in the car, I start asking her if there are little mini mansions in her neck of the woods.

There goes that raised eyebrow again. She's asking why, so I described to her what was described to me. She said something sounds off. If this negro lives around here, then he is exaggerating a tad bit. I can't imagine someone living in this particular neighborhood, spending what seemed to be large amounts of money for a legendary annual cookout. And besides, "I have never heard of any such event happening around here every year, but what do I know...." she sarcastically said. Welp, Joyce was right! We walked down the driveway into the backyard to what looked more like a scene from 'Don't be a Menace to South Central while Drinking Your Juice in the Hood' rather than a scene from a melanin's Martha's Vineyard soiree. I promise you that most of Cee's friends looked like they all had questionable pasts and priors to their names. There was a hazy cloud of smoke that began to fill this place, but it wasn't the same kind of smoke that filled the temple in the Bible. People were acting rowdy and yelled at each when talking, but I think that was because the music was so unnecessarily loud. You could barely hear one another speak! Although the music was hitting, the deejay only had one turntable and he wasn't even dee-jaying! (if that's even a real word). My man had a big ole plate of barbeque chicken, potato salad, and what looked like a delicious piece of salmon. *Well at least the food looks good.* When the music stopped he would put his cards face down on the table, casually get up from the spades game, go over to the music equipment and press a button and another song would come on. "This is absolute mayhem!" I yelled to my inner self. The music is never supposed to stop when you have a deejay! It seamlessly, and simultaneously just glides directly into the next song.

It looked liked everyone, and I mean just about everyone had a brown drink in their hand, and I'm like, "Really? This is *that* kinda party?" I haven't been at a party like this since college. I'm never a stick in the mud, but I have outgrown all of this and I expected that at the age of 47, he had too. Now here comes the silly in my head…"These jokers look like AARP members trying to audition for a Cardi B video. *All* these jokers look old, and why am I seeing a few canes up in here? These people better be careful because my CPR training has expired!"

When Cee saw us come in, he ran over and asked what had taken us so long to get there. "Hey ladies, where have you been? You're missing all the fun!" he boisterously stated.

"We started over an hour ago, and I told my mom you were coming and she's been looking for you. She wants to meet you." He blurted.

What?! What did he just say? "She wants to meet me? Why does your mother want to meet me?!" I asked puzzled.

"She wants to meet you because I've been *talking* to her about you girl," he responded as if to say, "Duh!!! Why wouldn't she want to meet you?"

Am I being punked? I started asking myself. And of course

now, I have to deal with Joyce. My beautifully quick-witted best friend is standing there beside me taking it all in and begins to stare at me with enlarged and questioning eyes when Cee announced that his mother was waiting to meet me. She looked at me like only Joyce can and now has this stupid smirk on her face. "His mom wants to meet you, DeeDee," she casually reminded me while tilting her head towards Cee's direction. "Yes DeeDee come on, mom has been waiting for you," he said as he introduced Joyce to one of his friends. Now I tilted my head at her and said with a phony smile on my face, "Okay Joycey, have fun with Mr. Bruce!"

Let me cut in here and make this long story short. Charles "Cee" Reagan turned out to be a complete weed-head! The business that he spoke of was a clothing store in downtown Newark that he lost because he and his girlfriend, who by the way was at the cookout, had broken up. (I'll include this drama in another book,,,Bye Felicia!) She was the majority owner and was the one who funded the daily expense of the store. He was the initial investor and secured the location of the clothing store. In his mind, he lost his 'stake in the company' due to a hostile takeover. The house turned out to be his mom's and he and his younger brother still lived with her. He said that he fell into a slight depression after losing the store and would smoke and workout as a release. What an oxymoron. During the day, after returning from the gym, he and a few friends would brainstorm ideas of how to make it back to the top. I told him he had a weed addiction and he should consider seeking help. Cee believed that he was not addicted because although he smokes weed daily, the substance grows from the earth so it is natural. He justifies and labels his drinking as a positive mood-booster that only occurs on the weekend. "Well Cee if you like it I love it, but it's not for me. I am not in that phase of life anymore and we have nothing in common. You're a cool dude, but not the man for me. This situation is over; take care of your-self. Goodbye."

You would not believe what a few of my friends said to me when I told them about Cee:

*DeeDee, you're always too hard on men!

*Girl your standards are too high. Learn how to compromise a little.

*Every man have an issue, so just get over it and work with what you have.

*Don't walk away and kick a dude while he is already down!

 *Maybe you are in his life as the beacon of light. You should be praying with him and helping him to get back on his feet.

*You used to drink and smoke weed too girl; you don't have the right to judge.

*Just because he's not as religious as you doesn't mean you can't be together. Don't throw the baby out with the bath water! Girl, he is workable.

I don't want this baby or the water he is bathing in! This is not what I want! He is not what I want! Since when did settling for just *anything* become the norm? Listen sis, if he is all that and a bag of your favorite chips, than you take him. I do have standards and non-negotiables.

Needless to say, Charles was definitely one of the many counterfeits that would enter and exit my life that year. There was Sean; a chocolate fine Jamaican background dancer for Usher that I met while vacationing in Montego Bay. I believe it was the beauty of the island, the short breaks and the quick get-a-ways from my daily routine in the U.S., and that sexy and sultry accent that almost got your girl caught up. However, I was rudely snapped back into reality when I received a phone call from his Canadian fiancée.

Then there was Marc. A very handsome, highly accomplished and sophisticated brother that I met when I partnered with a network marketing company. He had achieved a high rank within the company and often did presentations in my home market. The conversations were easy and refined. His perspective on life was refreshing, and I immensely enjoyed his zeal and desire to live an amazingly fulfilled life. He challenged my thought process and compelled me to want to grow more intellectually. He was a good one; a really good one. But Marc was also a recently divorced man, and although willing, he was not ready to jump immediately back into a committed relationship.

At his repeated request we attempted to try to see what the future would hold for us, but there was too much residue from his prior relationship. And that is to be expected. We both knew he needed to do the work of processing his experience, heal in the areas that had been damaged, and to do all of these endeavors while living a single life. It wouldn't be fair to Marc, or to myself, if we tried to force a relationship into existence when both individuals could not completely commit to it.

All of the men I dated believed in God. They all attended church; some more frequently than others. Each and every man was absolutely fine with me being a female pastor and supported the call on my life to serve in ministry. But they all were my warnings from God; they were the counterfeits. Remember, the enemy also knows what is about to enter your life and he will stop at nothing to hinder the manifestation. He will always send the counterfeit disguised as the blessing. Our job is to be watchful, aware, and ready...I WASN'T READY.

> *Be alert and of sober mind. Your enemy the devil prowls around like a roaring lion looking for someone to devour. -1 Peter 5:8*

CHAPTER

"SWEPT AWAY"

B ack to the chase of when 'Dorian met DeeDee.' "This guy seems cool. He's really nice Joyce," I smiled while telling her all about the conversation we had over dessert.

"Okay, that's nice and all, but calm down alright. You are so quick to like people! And I'm not just talking about guys, but *all* types of people. You are TOO NICE! I keep telling you that people aren't always who they appear to be. I know you call me the mean and cynical one, but I end up being right most of the time don't I?"

Joyce asked as she waited for the reply that I would give when I was listening but not trying to hear her at the moment, "Yeeeessssssss Joyce!" By the way, I think I am trusting and optimistic. I have been hurt and burned by past romantic relationships and some friendships as well, but I refuse to become bitter and paranoid. And now that I have such a close relationship with God, I'll be so much better in the selection process of allowing new people into my life and my immediate circle.

I had to fill Joyce in about all the details of Dorian. We already knew about him being a Pastor, and for me that fulfilled most of the character traits that I desired in anyone that I would consider dating. (And after dessert, the consideration was there). I knew what it meant for me to answer the call to become a Pastor. My late Pastor, and my current Pastor are my examples of true men and women of God. Both are people who live(d) exemplary lives before the Lord and I understand the mandate that exists for living above reproach because of these two.

Dorian had two children, a twelve year old daughter, and a 22 year old son. He said that since the divorce, he hadn't spent much time with his kids on account of their mother. He felt that she was poisoning their minds against him, the same way she had done half of the congregation at the church who abruptly left when she did. He shared that whenever he reached out to reconcile with them, he was rejected. They weren't handling the divorce well.

I am very careful about dating men with children. I had already raised my child and I did not have a desire to deal with baby-mama drama, or a budding teenager. I taught middle school for over fifteen years, and in my experience, if the household was not harmonious, the children usually displayed negative patterns of behavior. I cautiously kept this fact in mind. As a professional, Dorian was a project consultant and a soon-to-be author. It turned out that both Dorian and I were writing our first manuscripts and eventually shared portions of our books with one another. We were quickly learning that we had so much in common.

Joyce was happy that he was cool, but always kept that eyebrow in a raised high, salute position. He's seems quite nice, but if you decide to date him, just take it slow," she said.

"Yes ma'am," I responded. And I did. Try. I tried to take it slow, but he was so incredible that this *had* to be God. Dorian was the one! He had to be.

Dorian was so easy to talk to and he was actually very funny. I was pleasantly surprised at his humor because honestly, he was so old-fashioned in many ways. He would blame it on his strict, religious upbringing, but said that I was his breath of fresh air. I was so fun and carefree that he could finally be himself around me. The very next day after dessert, I began to awaken to the sweetest gif's and messages on my phone. Not a day would pass without a delightful morning salutation awaiting my morning rise. When we talked on the phone, or face-timed each other we ended up talking for hours at a time. A few days later he thought it only befitting to go on an official date. "Dinner or lunch?" he asked. I quickly chose lunch. Remember, your girl was trying to go slow and lunch was more casual. He asked what time I would be ready and like clockwork, he and his chariot were outside and waiting.

Dorian had insisted on taking me home on the night that we had dessert, and with the abundance of information I had gathered on him, I felt it was fine. He asked to meet my mother to see if she would approve of him, and she of course loved every minute of their conversing. Always the perfect gentlemen, he opened every door from the house to the car to the restaurant. He actually noticed and addressed that I always went to grab the car door before he could get to it. "I notice that you instinctively attempt to open doors for yourself," he said.

"Well how else am I going to get through them? I've been doing this for a few years, and I'm a big girl. I can open up a door." I laughed.

"Now that I'm here, you will never open your own car door; or any other door for that matter. You will never have to carry anything but your purse, and if you want me to carry that too, it wouldn't be a problem." He responded. *Who is this guy?* I would find myself, asking myself, over and over again.

We ate lunch at the Cheesecake Factory and shared some of our food. I had some of his potatoes and I gave him a couple of shrimp. When he ordered the steak I was almost embarrassed. During our first conversation over dessert at the diner, we talked about our favorite foods. His was steak and mine was shrimp. I told him that although I am not a vegan, I try to keep beef at bay and only eat red meat about once or twice a year. *I try to hold out for the cookouts in the summer.* He said that he too only ate meat about once every year. His church hosts an annual bus ride to the Shopping Outlets and to an all-you-can eat buffet where they serve the best steaks on the planet. So needless to say, when he ordered the steak I almost blushed. He must really be smitten with me. He's going to use his once-a-year steak allotment on our lunch date? Well in the words of Johnny Gill, *"My, My, My!"* I thought.

After an enjoyable lunch, I asked if we could run into the mall to check out the Mac makeup store. There was a particular color that I could only find there, but I would understand if he felt uncomfortable going to that store. He said he was fine. The most perfect lipstick color that I wanted was sold out. The salesperson checked to see if Nordstrom's had the color, but to no avail. She reported back that this particular color was about to be discontinued so when I do find it, I should grab a bunch. Would you believe that we went to Sephora? at Dorian's request! "Is there another store that we could try? Maybe they carry a similar color," he suggested. "Absolutely! There is definitely another place we could try," I replied surprisingly. I didn't think this man would want to go on a lipstick hunt, but when he offered, I gladly accepted. When we arrived at Sephora, *Dorian* took the initiative to locate a salesperson, show her the half emptied tube of my

'Cist' colored lipstick, and proceeded to help her search through the various shades in the store to find the one closest to mine. Disappointed, yet simultaneously pleased with such an effort, we left the store without any lipsticks in tow, but we continued to walk the mall while talking, laughing, and continuing to learn about each other.

While riding back to my house, Dorian wanted to know when we could see each other again. He already knew I had a full plate so he was willing to take whatever time I was willing to give. In addition to the church and my teaching responsibilities, I told him that my main area of focus was on building my team with my new networking business. Most of my free time would be dedicated to first studying, and then reaching a new rank in my company. I was a millionaire in the making so reading, studying and personal development were key for me. He understood and said he would be in touch.

The next day, a beautiful arrangement of edible fruits were delivered to my house, along with a note recalling my love of all things fruit. "This was very nice, Dorian," I thought while commencing to dive into the fruit concoction. Two days after this, another package arrived for me in the mail, but I hadn't ordered anything. The return label read, 'Mac Cosmetics, New York, NY. "No... he... did... not!" I shouted while prying open this securely taped UPS brown box. Inside of this box was another small box that I had to rip apart. *Get to it already!* Finally opened, and under a mound of shredded paper were two gorgeous tubes of 'Cist' lipstick with a note that read, "I would have purchased more but these were the last two in stock." What in the world?! "Okay now wait a minute, what the heck is going on God? Is this man for real? Is he a counterfeit because I'm about to like him a lot!!! He can't be! What man do you know on this planet, will go online to search out a discontinued lipstick color for someone he just met?" *Let me call Joyce…*

She was impressed and the gifts of affection continued to come. The next week at work during my lunch break, I was called down to the office. I walked inside and saw the most amazing bouquet of yellow roses and said to the secretary, "Someone is going to be happy with those!" She responded, "Yes I know. That someone is you." "Seriously, those are for me?" I squealed. "Yes they are. Two dozen of roses! That's why you were called to the office, to pick up your flowers. Looks like you have an admirer," she smiled.

"I guess I do," I concurred.

The texts messages with all kinds of thoughtful prayers and quotes, the Hallmark cards with loving thoughts of me, more flowers and packages delivered, and the amazing dinner dates had all begun to melt my heart.

"Dorian, what are you doing? You do not have to shower

me with gifts. I don't want you to think that I'm all about gaining material things from a man." I said over the phone.

"I know that you are not materialistic and you can unquestionably get all of these things for yourself, and that's one of the reasons I enjoy showering you with my affections. I want to be the man that gives you the world. I really like you DeeDee. I like you a lot, and I want you to understand that I have extremely strong feelings for you. When a man knows what he wants, he goes after it, and I want you," he said with so much swag that I had to sit down and fan myself.

Like any normal person in my situation I began to think, think, and overthink some more. I started to get a headache from all the thinking and consideration I was giving to this situation. My thoughts were getting out of control, and I was beginning to feel overwhelmed! I want to be in the complete and perfect will of God for my life. I can't mess up again and choose wrong. I will never go through another divorce! Almost daily I pondered on what to do and these were only part of my thoughts:

*Do I want to be in a committed relationship right now?

*I need to focus on me. But God did say that He was preparing me to be a wife.

*A wife? You guys aren't even in a relationship yet so be easy!

*But you know that's what he wants; he is very persistent.

*I have no time for counterfeits, and he could very well be one.

*This dude was married for over twenty years in an unhappy marriage, so he must be a man of commitment. He is in it for the long haul.

"DeeDee just chill out and breathe. You are overthinking this thing," everyone, including Dorian would say to me. Calm yourself down and learn to relax. You got this! Enjoy the journey ahead of you. I took a few deep breaths and realized I was operating in what my mother always said *not* to do; "DeeDee, don't make a mountain out of a mole-hill!" I took a deep breath and submitted to the road that lay ahead of me. Dorian was chasing and I was walking really fast, but I believe the gesture that finally took me over the edge happened on one snowy night in the middle of the week.

We were on the phone, everyday now as usual, and I told Dorian that I was hungry and tired. Dorian asked why I hadn't eaten yet and I told him that I was busy making calls and securing meetings for potential customers. He then asked me, "DeeDee, what would you like to eat for dinner?" "Red Lobster," I sleepily replied. "I've been wanting shrimp for over a week now," I smiled. "But I'm going to go grab something in a minute," I said. We continued with our casual conversation and discussed all the prior events of our day. The next thing I know, he says, "Girl did you eat something yet? I haven't heard you chewing or anything." "No sir. I didn't feel like going downstairs." I replied.

"I didn't think so. Go grab your coat and come outside," he laughed. "WHAT?! What in the world are you talking about?" I yelled.

He said, "Come outside. I came to take you to Red Lobster!"

Now you must remember that Dorian lives an hour away from me, AND it was snowing outside! I jumped off the bed and ran to the window. When I snatched the curtain back I could not believe what I was seeing. There was Dorian's car, smack dab in the middle of the street with his hazard lights on, and him getting out of the car with an opened umbrella in hand walking to my porch. What in the world is this man doing?" I screamed. I ran downstairs to open the door and he was just there, standing on my porch smiling and asking me if I was ready to go to dinner.

"What are you doing here?" I asked him while simultaneously jumping around trying to find my coat. *My sleepy behind woke right on up!*

He said, "Aren't you the one who's been wanting shrimp from Red Lobster? Well I came to take you to Red Lobster."

"But it's snowing outside! Why would you come all the way here in the snow? Driving in the snow could be dangerous!" I fussed.

"I don't see snow DeeDee; all I see is you," Dorian replied.

And there you have it, ladies and gentlemen. The broom of love had come in and swept my silly self straight up off my feet.

From that moment on, Dorian and DeeDee became an official couple! He finally convinced me that he must be the one!

> With patience a ruler may be persuaded, and a soft tongue will break a bone. —Proverbs 25:15 ESV

CHAPTER SEVEN

"RED FLAGS"

We were talking every day on the phone, and seeing each other almost every other day. I felt this was senseless because of the distance. I thought he was doing too much and pushing too fast. When I shared my feelings with those I trust, I was made to feel like I was the one overreacting or reading too much into everything.

"You're just not used to all of this attention from a *good* man. This is what good men do! You finally have the knight in shining armor that we all wait for, and now you don't know what to do with him. There have been nothing but counterfeits and suddenly you can't trust in the real thing when it comes!"

These were the voices that consistently lingered in my head from everyone to my single friends, to my married friends, my mentors, and myself. I know there is safety in a multitude of counsel so I needed to ensure that I was giving due diligence to the matter at hand. I would often ask Dorian directly, "Isn't this going too fast? What would you advise a member of your church to do if they were in our position?" Dorian quickly reassured me that he *would* recommend that they slow things down, but that they were not us. God had spoken to him clearly about us, and I needed to trust him.

He decided to join my network marketing team just to be able to spend more time with me. He had previously partnered with this same company before, but chalked it up to not being the most opportune time for him to build a business. Dorian also began to help me build *my* business. He began to recruit some of everybody! One of the best nights for me was when I hit the first rank or level in my business. Dorian had asked me out to dinner, but I had plans to 'show the plan' at a team mixer that night. Insistent on seeing me because he missed me so much, he decided to wait. "No problem, I will wait for you. We can go out when you're done," was his reply. "We can go out some other night Dorian, it's going to be late." I suggested. But he wouldn't take no for an answer.

Mixers normally lasted for 2-3 hours and I figured that I would be finished by 9pm or 9:30pm. I worked my behind off in that meeting, secured three more business partners, and this allowed me to hit the first notable rank in my company! It was one of the best feelings of accomplishment! The meeting ended around 11 o'clock and of course Dorian was outside of my house still waiting for me when I pulled up onto my block. I excitedly told him all about the mixer and even about the congratulatory call I received from one of the leaders in the company! This night could not get any better. We went out to dinner and on this night, we shared our first passionate kiss. Something I told myself I would not do again while in a relationship. I allowed myself to get caught up in the high of winning! I knew it was too late to be out with this man.

I had already decided to refrain from passionate kissing, or anything remotely sexual that could open a door to sin. *Been there, done that!* My concern was not only Dorian, but DeeDee. This standard was for me. I had to set boundaries and parameters for myself and learn to practice being firm in my decisions. Dorian recalled how he could remember not having any feelings of desire for his first wife. Prior to them meeting one another, he prayed to be delivered from feelings of lust and since he noticed those feelings were absent concerning her, he was grateful for his deliverance. He could finally build a solid relationship on friendship, trust, and God. He later understood that he was not *ever* attracted to her, and that he should have had sexual desires towards her because it was natural. *Our love* for one another was strong and powerful and his desires for me were *natural*. He promised to respect my wishes and that we would remain abstinent. Dorian assured me of his respect for my standards; there would be no sex before marriage. But shouldn't this be his standard as well? He was a man of God. He was a Pastor. Why am I the only one who has established guidelines and mandates that honor my dedication and commitment to God? This was a huge red flag for me, so why did I stay? What was it within DeeDee that allowed me not to value my standards or my worth?

Shortly thereafter, Dorian began to confess his love for me and I began to confess my love for him. He said that the Lord told him I was his treasure. Dorian shared with me how shortly after meeting me, there was a necessity to sit before the Lord concerning me. Although it had been his routine to fast every Wednesday, he said he bowed his knees and submitted to the Lord in prayer. He earnestly prayed and asked, "God, Who Is She?" The Lord had given him a scripture. *Matthew 13:44 "The kingdom of heaven is like a treasure hidden in a field. When a man found it, he hid it again, and then in his joy went and sold all he had and bought that field.* "DeeDee, you are my treasure. For you it may appear that I am moving fast, and I apologize if I ever made you uncomfortable in any way. The lengthy conversations I initiate, our serious topics of discussion, the sharing of my dreams for our future together, are all intentional. There is motive behind my actions. After clearly hearing from God, I am preparing to buy my field; to acquire my treasure. I am expeditiously arranging my personal affairs and securing all loose ends in my life. I am preparing to marry you. You are my treasure. I am not the counterfeit Dee; I am a man who perceives the value in you. You allow me to be who I really am and for this I am eternally grateful.

But if we are to be completely honest with one another, there are times that I began to wonder about us as well. The nine years between us appeared to be more significant than I originally thought. My experience in life drastically supersedes yours and it is becoming apparent that we function on two different levels of maturity. The possibility is that you are simply not ready for my type of love. You refuse to accept the key to my apartment but I am trying to establish trust with you. I could become slightly offended that you believe my sexual desires for you and corresponding advances are inappropriate. I am a man DeeDee; yes, a man of God, but still a virile man who is strongly attracted to a strikingly beautiful woman. I deem it necessary to remind *you* of my initial lack of notice with regard to your sensual and shapely pulchritude. I understand your previous relationships were challenging and now it is obvious that your trust is damaged. But I am not here to hurt you. I am the one who came to take away all the pain caused by those who have mishandled your heart. Maybe you need to consider if you are indeed ready for my love," Dorian shared. (Red flag number two)

I am now viewed as immature because I chose to uphold the standards that were put in place by God? Now I'm not ready for a relationship because I want to do things in a way that will please God and bring honor to him? Dorian would remind me that he had been pastoring a church for 13 years and I had just begun my journey. I was a stickler for the Bible and the mandates written within, but he and his friends in the faith had a different perspective. I began to meet his circle of friends and they all had his same views; the men and the women. I should loosen up, lighten up, and live life. God loves, and He forgives was there basic message. *My* people already thought I was too much when it came to God, and now I'm meeting others from a different circle who agreed more with my friends than with me. I began to rethink my 'rules and standards.' Maybe I was a little too rigid and uptight. Even a female pastor friend of his admitted to slipping up a little here and there with her now husband before they were actually married. They had already decided to get married and were engaged so it wasn't that bad. God would later remind me that all of this was unquestionably wrong. This was compromise, it was not pleasing to Him, and I had better listen to the voice of God and not to the voices of man.

I decided, against my better judgment, to take the advice of everyone else and go with the flow. When you're the anomaly in the group, you can begin to believe that you are the one who is wrong.

Dorian and I began to do almost everything together! If you saw me, you would see him. Walks in the park, horseback riding, arcades and games, movies, of course church, and our infamous dinner dates. I recall one of the first times, early in the relationship, that I saw something contrary, but I said nothing. This was another red flag; number three, that I saw, but ignored.

The second time that we went out to eat, Dorian had ordered steak. I raised my Joyce eyebrow remembering that Dorian stated he only ate red meat once a year. It stood out to me because I remembered feeling so special when he ordered steak on our first official date, but now he's ordering steak again? For the second time in a row? I know, I know. You are most likely thinking, "What's the big deal about eating steak?" NOTHING!!! Absolutely nothing at all. That's the point! There is no big deal except for the fact that you were *adamant* about only eating red meat once a year. So why are we on steak number two? What this says to me is that you were dishonest with me. What I believe is maybe you just said that to impress me. But why would your culinary preferences impress me? You could eat the entire butcher shop and I wouldn't care!

As I began to think about it, it appears that you'll say anything you think I want to hear. Just because I choose not to consume a lot of red meat, doesn't me that you can't.

This steak situation bothered me so much that I went to God and prayed about this thing. I couldn't let it go! God told me the minute you mention this to Dorian he will never order steak again. And of course God was right. After he ordered steak for the fifth time I said to him, "Dorian I thought you said you only ate red meat once a year and I've noticed that you've ordered steak every single time that we've gone out to eat." He had this look on his face of embarrassment, perplexity, and offense. He said, "Really, I hadn't noticed." And from that moment on, you guessed it people; he ordered everything from the rooter to the tooter but never again steak! During every other dinner date we went on there was chicken, fish, pork, shrimp, lobster, veal, and any other piece of meat that exists, but not steak.

I said, "God you know I can't stand a liar so what is this? Is Dorian a liar because if so, I am done with this relationship! This is over!"

DeeDee it is only steak! Are you seriously going to end what is otherwise a great relationship over steak? Girl, gather yourself! You are actually trying to find something wrong with this man. He is *not* too good to be true. This is no big deal. I guess he really wants me to like him.

Once again I thought I was reading too much into everything. I started to talk myself out of believing what I was witnessing. Taking a deep breath and attempting not to sabotage a

Godly relationship, I made one simple request. God, if he is not the one, please show me and make it clear. God did.

Portia Campbell. We will refer to her here as Ms. Portia Campbell. Dorian's ex-girlfriend. She apparently is the main reason he once believed that all women must be crazy. He tells the story of the severe pain and heartache she caused him. They had met over fifteen years ago while working in the same department at Saint Plains Hospital in New York. There were a group of them that would get together during lunch and a close bond was formed within that circle. She was an ear when he needed to vent about his unhappy marriage but it was nothing more than a true friendship. While in the process of divorcing his first wife, Portia was a huge help with a major crisis that surfaced in Dorian's life. Both of his parents had become ill at the same time, and since his immediate family was not as helpful, Portia stepped in and became his lifesaver. She was his anchor and support during one of the roughest moments in his life. As she began to become the sanity in what appeared to be an insane life circumstance, they began to see each other as more than just friends. His children, especially his baby-girl, fell in love with her and she in love with them. Her children adored Dorian and this was the life he desired to live. His heart had found its home. Dorian's parents were so thankful for her being such a wonder in his life, and Dorian believed that Portia was most definitely the one for him. When he decided to talk to his mother and tell her of his intentions towards Portia, he said he'd received such a shock. Dorian's mom was known for having keen wisdom and a sensitive discerning spirit. She had a way of knowing the true heart and intent of a person, and according to Dorian mom was NEVER wrong. Dorian told his mom of his plans to marry Portia, but mom blatantly said, "No son. She is not the one." Dorian was certain that his mother would agree with his choice. She and Portia had a great friendship and Portia helped her with whatever needs she had, so Dorian was completely surprised; but he knew his mother was always right. He decided not to propose and within a few months he discovered that Portia was sleeping with someone else. Not only had she betrayed his heart, but the gentleman she had been with was supposed to have been dead! Yes! You heard me, DEAD! At some point earlier in their friendship, details of their prior lives and relationships were shared. Portia had children from previous men and one of those men had supposedly lost his life. I am unsure of the details surrounding his death, but Portia said he died several years ago. Well, I assume he had a Lazarus spirit because he came back from the dead that night! Portia told Dorian that everyone thought this man was dead and he just showed up back in her life.

Dorian and Portia were supposed to meet up one night, but she never showed. No call, no text, no Portia. Dorian said he had already believed that something wasn't quite right with them lately and his intuition told him she was being untruthful. She had, "Conveyed signs of deception" as Dorian would say.

As Dorian recounted the sordid particulars of this fiasco he mentioned something about Portia that made me question his continued involvement with her. As if it were of no importance or significance Dorian blurted out, "I should have known she was crazy when she was trying to get me to use crystals."

"CRYSTALS!" I yelled. "Are you serious? That's witchcraft! You *do* know that right? What did she do?" I harshly quizzed him. I needed to know how far this went!

"Of course I know it is witchcraft, DeeDee. My uncle was a deliverance minister and taught me everything I know on the subject. I used to work with him in his meetings," Dorian reminded me. " She was persuasive but I refrained."

"Why would you stay with someone who practices beliefs that are the exact opposite of yours? You should have left her alone then!" I complained. "She could've poisoned your food or something crazy! What were you thinking?" I asked.

"Those Spanish women are a totally different breed," he said laughingly. "They will have you doing some of everything!" he laughed. I didn't find anything funny. Especially not the realization that you were aware of her practices, and as a Pastor you were okay with it? Your family and your congregation could have been at risk.

Dorian said after he ended their relationship she made several attempts to win back his love. She was persistent. Portia sent cards, apologies, had meetings with his mom, but eventually after no avail, she had gotten the point. Or at least he thought.

Dorian and I were on the phone talking while he drove back to New York after one of our dates. We would talk until he got in the house and then we'd Face-time each other before bed. This had become our routine to ensure his safe arrival home after having such a long day. This night was different. Dorian's voice suddenly changed and he began to talk as if he were now preoccupied. I heard a woman in the background and she was calling his name.

"Dorian, where are you and who is that calling you?" I asked.

"It's Portia. She is in my parking garage and apparently she's been waiting for me," he responded. My heart dropped into my stomach. *"What the heck is going on?"* I thought. I do not have time for this right now. *Is he is messing around, Lord?!*

After everything this man has been saying to me! Alright. Wait a minute and let me stay calm DeeDee.

"Why is she waiting for you?" I asked.

"DeeDee I have no idea. She is saying she needs to talk to me. Let me go so I can handle this situation. I'll call you back when I get inside," he said.

"Oh no you won't. I'm staying on the phone so I can hear what she is saying! You said she is crazy right, so if she decides to get stupid I can be a witness and call the police if I have to! Don't let her know you're on the phone," I said.

Now that's what I told Dorian, but DeeDee was not

hanging up that phone because there is ALWAYS two sides to the story and I was about to hear hers. Dorian agreed and since he wore a Bluetooth headset, she did not even realize that he was on the phone. Portia was screaming at him and asking why he won't return her calls and how could he ignore her after all they have been through.

"Yes Lord!" I thought. A sense of relief overtook me when I heard her pleading with him because she had been ignored and I was so proud of Dorian; Proud to be his lady. He was the real deal! Dorian was telling her to calm down and go home.

"We are over Portia. We have been over for a long time now. I will not continue to engage in these senseless conversations with you. Please go home," my baby said.

"Over? I know we're broken up Dorian, but you just slept with me last month so how is it now over?!" Portia yelled.

"What the @#%& did she just say!" I thought. I began profusely shaking my head as if to unscramble the words I just heard, and to un-see the visuals that were now torturing my mind. I was beyond livid! *"Don't say a word DeeDee! Act like you didn't hear the craziness that she just said so he can continue this conversation. I want to hear it all!"* I spoke to myself.

"Portia, I don't know what you're talking about! Just go home, we are over! I am not with you anymore," he said sounding like a stupid fool.

"You were with me last month! In your apartment Dorian,

you don't remember that? And suddenly you just stop answering your phone! You can't talk to me? You're going to talk to me!" Portia said sounding just as heartbroken as I now was.

Their conversation lasted another five minutes and I honestly can't recall how it ended. My mind had shut down after I heard the phrase *'slept with me last month'*. While they continued to argue back and forth, every romantic dinner date, the constant deliveries of red roses and arrangements to my job and home, his sweet text messages, the hour-long conversations of laughter, our sharing of hopes and dreams for the future flashed across my eyes. All I could see were Dorian's deep brown eyes that had once been brought to tears as he declared his unfailing love for me...

"You lying little nigga," I said just as calm as a cool cucumber. You told me the last time you were in a relationship was last year, and you slept with ole girl last month!" I said as my voice perpetually raised in volume.

"It was last year!" he squealed.

"Are you freaking kidding me? You have got to be crazy and out of your freaking mind to sit here and have the nerve to try and say because last month was December and we're now in January, that it was LAST YEAR!!!" I screamed. You fake lying so called Pastor! That ain't no LAST YEAR you stupid liar! And you're just sleeping with her like that? You are such a phony nigga! You can't even say that you two were in a loving and committed relationship, and that one or two times y'all slipped up! Not that it makes it any better, but you stand in front of a congregation every Sunday morning like it's nothing! You pray over people and then put your nasty stinking hands on them! Do you have no scruples?! Obviously this is just what you do!

This is over Dorian. Do not call my phone, do not text me, and do lose my number! I am done with you." CLICK....

> *Do not lie to one another, for you have stripped off the old self with its evil practices. -Colossians 3:9 (AMP)*

CHAPTER EIGHT

"MANIPULATION 101"

It was completely over. I refused to answer Dorian's call or respond to any of his text messages. As far as I was concerned I had seen the true man and when people show you who they are, believe them! That's what our magnificent Maya Angelou taught us to do. Believe who they are, at that very exact moment. Not to believe in whom you want them to be, or even whom they proclaim they desire to become.

Of course I was disappointed and my heart was hurt, but I was in pretty decent shape. Besides, this was a short –lived, whirlwind romance. We met each other in January and it was over by the end of February. *Thank you Lord for not having wasted so much of my time.* But the funny thing is, I had to remind my heart to stop feeling pain. "What is wrong with you? Snap out of it! It is what it is, and we're going to be just fine. You have endured much worse, so get yourself together beautiful lady," I would say to encourage myself on the days where flash-backs of times together made an assassination attempt on my heart. How could Dorian's grand over-the-top gestures and continuous professions of love for me seem so genuine when they were not? Breathe girl, and move on. And I did, but the constant questioning of what happened to you two did not assist with the healing process. Dorian and I had become such an item privately, and then publicly. The question of, "Where's Dorian?" often followed the greeting of *Hi DeeDee*, or *Greetings Pastor DeeDee*. I knew how important it was to choose my words carefully concerning Dorian. The church community is quick to remind you 'Not to put your mouth on the *mand* or woman of God!' My responses were generic, yet true. I decided a long time ago that if I was going to lie and displease God, that the lie wouldn't be wasted on someone else. "Pastor Dorian is in New York somewhere, doing only God knows what. Pastors are always so busy you know," I laughed and grinned as they displayed their agreement with a reciprocal smile. Handling the public was easy; the private, not so much.

I was regretting the conversation I had to have with Joyce. I was not in the mood at all for her annoying, piercing eyebrows, the awkward quiet moments in the conversation, and the *I keep telling your behind to slow it down'* lecture. But I had to surrender to it because it couldn't be avoided any longer. And like only a true best friend would do, she literally bombarded my space and time with big hugs, hallmark cards that make you cry, and little trinkets like mugs and stationary with reminders of how awesome I am, and how she would always love me and be there for me no matter what. I am guessing my Sunday morning sermons are beginning to soften her heart a bit. Another thing that surprised me was most of the Godly wisdom and advice I received from a few of my close church friends and mentors.

She probably seduced him. I know she did.

These Jezebels know he is taken but they don't care! You have to watch out for those garden tools. (This is the 'saved way' to call them hoes.)

He is a great guy DeeDee. He was probably too scared to tell you the truth in fear that you would judge him.

His first marriage was such a monstrosity and she gave him such a hard time. She broke his spirit and then you came and breathed life back into him. He needs you.

You have to forgive him because that is the Godly thing to do.

You know he is the one for you! Look at all the signs of how you two met!

Why would you let such a good man get away? Girl you are crazy, and too picky!

*All of the grace and forgiveness you gave to the wrong men, should be extended to him because he is The One!

*Give him a chance to tell his side of the story. The least you could do is hear him out.

*Don't let the enemy take what belongs to you!!! Go back and get your man from that harlot!

I became confused. I thought God was speaking by revealing the actions of this man. I wasn't wrong, they were wrong! I understand that these are people of God with far greater anointings than mine, and a considerable amount of more experience in ministry under their belts than me, but I hear God too! I know how he speaks and Dorian's actions were not aligned with His word so I am positive that I am not in error regarding my decisions. And then, manipulation veered its ugly little head. If you are not literally taught and trained on this topic of manipulation, you will get deceived every single time.

I was persuaded to acquiesce and allow Dorian to have his side of the story heard. He was posting subliminal messages on social media, and had spoken to mutual friends of ours (the friends I met via him) and the consensus was out. Give him another chance. Everyone felt sorry for him. What about me?

I did not want to see Dorian so we determined that a phone discussion would suffice. Dorian did apologize for my feelings getting hurt in the midst of his attempts to end his previous relationship, but not for his actions. His response was that his final indiscretion with Portia did indeed occur during last year's time. The calendar year had ended and so had his dealings with Portia. "We both know to 'forget those things that are behind us' and to give our attention to what is now before us." I in no uncertain terms ended my relationship with Portia, but she was having an arduous time accepting my resolution. I should not be held responsible and penalized for someone else's careless actions. Portia is an emotionally unstable woman and is extreme in her displays of feelings towards me. I wish you never had to hear her ridiculous laments and absurdities," he said calmly and with an assurance. "And for that I am deeply sorry. But I will not permit you to judge me DeeDee!" he stated as he raised his voice. "I have repented for my actions and only God is the one I need to make amends with concerning Portia. You and I had yet to meet one another. All of this hysteria with Portia occurred before I ever laid eyes on you, so you speaking to me in such a harsh manner is completely unwarranted. I have had time to think and God reminded me to not receive the spirit of guilt. You yourself are not exactly an innocent little angel. We both have a past remember. Before we met you shared with me a time, that since you were a pastor, that you and another man did more than share an evening's kiss goodbye, so where was your self-righteousness then PASTOR

DeeDee?" he asked while awaiting my clap back.

"Wow Dorian really! You are going to turn this around on me?" I replied.

"No I am not DeeDee, I am just stating the facts here," he said with a grin on his face. I could see it through the phone. "First of all if we are going to go there, then let's go with the complete truth. I told you that on *one occasion*, not several as it was with you and your ex-girlfriend, but one, that my friend and I went a little too far one night. I immediately ended the relationship, and there was no going back and forth about it. It was over and I told him that I could not compromise myself like this. I wouldn't be able to stand in front of the people and speak a thing! I made it clear that I could not do this so I walked away. I repented to God that night and begged for His forgiveness," I said defending myself, but now feeling like crap.

"I have been distraught at the thought of possibly losing you. I reluctantly posted on social media because of your refusal to speak with me. I did so with the hopes of you reading my messages and giving me another chance. I am so deeply sorry for the pain I've caused you DeeDee. I am head over heels in love with you and my desire is that we can be together; we are meant for one another and you know this is true. You can even reflect back on how we met one another. That was the will of God. He is in control, not us. I am a different man when I am in your presence.

You allow me to be who I really am, and I need that. I can be silly with you, you allow me to express myself, and I need you in my life. Please don't allow our past mistakes to forgo a wonderful future together. Can we both forgive one another and give our love the fighting chance that it deserves? Allow me another chance to prove my unwavering love for you?" he now pleaded. What the heck am I forgiving him for? What did I do? See the truth!

(Sidebar; I had lost count of the amount of red flags that were waved, thrown out, and smacking me in the face by now.)

I promised that I would pray about it and get back to him, either way, with my answer. Perplexed, confused, almost disoriented does not adequately describe my thoughts and feelings during this time of prayer. One minute I thought I heard God, and the next I wasn't so sure. Too many voices, including my own, were clouding my thoughts. If I walk away could I miss out on the love of a lifetime? I have never had a Godly man treat me like such a princess. This man dotes over me, lavishes me with gifts, spends every free moment with me, and he hasn't hid that from anyone. But God I believe you pulled the curtain back on this situation with Portia to show me the truth! I felt as if my breath was literally being extracted from my body. I have to give this man an answer. He continually texts and calls to reassure me that he isn't going anywhere, and that I am who he wants. Forever.

Maybe I should have fasted more. Perhaps my lack of patience that often proceeds some of my decisions has surfaced once more. Regardless of what has transpired and what has been said, Dorian was right about one thing. I had fallen short of the glory of God in my own life. This was a reality and it began to haunt me. I had an indiscretion as well and God forgave me. He gave me another chance, so I should do the same for Dorian.

Dorian and I reconnected and if you think he displayed his affections for me before, you ain't seen nothing yet! The dinner dates became even more romantic and opulent, and I think he tried to introduce me to everyone he knew. He wanted to assure me that I was aware of everyone in his life, and that everyone in his world knew about the love of his life. He also endeavored to whisk me away on a vacation weekend. He practically begged me to go away with him to Vegas. "Absolutely not!" I refused repeatedly when asked. "I am not going on a vacation with a man who is not my husband. Been there and done that Dorian. It's too much temptation. You have to fight this flesh hard to maintain your celibacy. The environment alone is conducive for sex and everything else. No Dorian, sorry. And it doesn't look right and I don't want anyone getting the wrong idea about us. The bible says to shun the very appearance of evil," I reminded him.

"There you go again DeeDee. You are too funny sometimes. We haven't had sex and we will not have sex until we get married, but fine DeeDee. I relinquish my dreams of Vegas and I will leave it alone; for now," he sighed.

Dorian and I continued on with our love affair, and all was well within our world; for the most part. Dorian was a tender, kind, and gentle man. At times I wondered if I were starring in a romantic movie set in the 1940's. He was a gentleman's man. He absolutely enjoyed flowering me with compliments and whispering sweet nothings in my ear. But from time to time though, I would ask myself if Dorian was everything that I wanted in a man. I would consider the idea that Dorian would be the absolute perfect guy for someone else, but not for me. It was a challenge for me to fully embrace all of his idiosyncrasies and quirky mannerisms. Honestly some of Dorian's displays of affection towards me were melodramatic and a complete turn off.

What he believed to be hot–like-fire, was nothing more than corny and old-fashioned to me. I am reminded of a time when we were sitting in his car after returning to my house from a wonderful evening out. He looked lovingly into my eyes and caressed my face in the most feminine of ways and began to utter his words of adoration. I actually stopped him, mid-sentence, and asked him if he was gay. He appeared unoffended and extremely confident in his response. "No DeeDee, I am not gay. I am a mere mature man who appreciates the finer things in life. I am a consummate lover of words and I happen to possess the ability to express myself using the proper King's James Language. It genuinely excites me!" he stated.

"Well it doesn't excite me. I need a little more swag in my life," I countered.

"Okay Dorian, we have promised one another to be completely honest, even with the touchy subjects that could potentially be hurtful or embarrassing. And I also want to remind you, before we continue with this conversation, that it is always you who wants to discuss our truest and deepest feelings; to explore the depths of our souls together, as you would say; so here goes my soul. At certain times when you express yourself to me, I don't find it a turn on like you do. Let's look at it this way. You can be more like Barry Manilow, and I'm simply asking if Jodeci can surface from time to time," I smiled. He thought I was so cute and he started cracking up laughing, but I was serious. We both started laughing and being reminded of our age differences. I teased him asking, "Do you even know who Jodeci is? If not, try channeling Barry White more often, and not Manilow."

I know Dorian loves utilizing his expansive vocabulary and I actually liked knowing that I could learn so much from him. I do like intelligent men; teach me baby! But I think it bothers me at times because I sensed it was more for him than for me. I sensed he needed to feel important and revered by people.

Then I began to feel bad and remembered that I must not be so picky. Shoot, I am positive there has to be plenty of things I do, or fail to do that he may not agree with, and he is not complaining so why should I. Remember the saying, "Don't make the minor things major. Or don't major in the minor things; something like that right," I thought. He was a great guy, *a different one*, but nonetheless great. You will grow and learn to love *everything* about him over time. Let him be free to be himself. If that corniness makes him happy, then let him be corny *and* happy. You have to accept people for who they are, and it's really not that big of a deal. Any other woman would love to have a Dorian, with his overly expressive self, in their lives. What woman doesn't love the complete attention, respect, and honor of her man towards her? Women are quick to give lectures on needing a man who can actually communicate his thoughts and feelings. Dorian most certainly has this down-pat. But DeeDee, are you compromising your own wishes and desires again, or simply just compromising?

> *Such people are not serving Christ our Lord; they are serving their own personal interests. By smooth talk and glowing words they deceive innocent people. Romans 16:18 (NLT)*

CHAPTER

"THE ENGAGEMENT"

A couple of days before my pastoral anniversary weekend, Dorian and I got into a heated argument. I was very tired and did not feel like 'exploring the depths of our feelings and emotions' that night and Dorian felt slighted. 'I oftentimes postulate, am I the only one who is completely invested in this relationship DeeDee," he snarled.

"What? Can you speak English please! I don't feel like grabbing a dictionary in order to talk to you tonight, Dorian. I already told you that I am tired and I want to go to sleep. I had a very long day and my schedule tomorrow is going to be hectic as well. Why can't we continue this conversation later?" I begged.

"This is exactly what I'm referring to when I state that sometimes I feel our age differences are an issue. A relationship requires time, commitment, and sacrifice and I perceive you are severely lacking in these areas. You commit yourself to everyone else but me. Your business partners, Joyce, your church members all get more of your time than I do. You need to evaluate yourself and your efforts towards me," he barked.

"Are you serious right now?" I think you are over exaggerating, Dorian. I am doing the same things I was doing when we met. Am I now supposed to pause my life because you're in it?" I sternly asked.

"I have greatly sacrificed for you DeeDee and yes, I am certain that you are just not ready for my type of love," he said once again.

"Well you know what Dorian, maybe I'm not! I can't do this with you anymore. This is too much for me. I don't want this anymore. I'm done." Click ...

Dorian tried to call me back, but I was physically drained and could not bring myself to answer the phone. Maybe he was right though. I'm probably not mature enough to understand the substantial requirements necessary to build a long-lasting relationship. His mature type of love is overbearing at times and yeah, I'm not ready for it at all. I'll have to be okay with this and move on because I just can't do this with him anymore. I'm literally exhausted; emotionally, mentally, and physically. I need a vacation.

But the title of this chapter is THE ENGAGEMENT???
I know, I know. How could there possibly be an engagement after
all of this turmoil you may be asking? This narrative should have
ended at Chapter 8; the number of new beginnings, but we were
just getting started.

The weekend had been amazing! My anniversary services
thus far were absolutely phenomenal and this upcoming Sunday
was going to be off the chain! God had been blowing our minds
all weekend! My first lady came and shut it down when she
preached a sermon about the significance of my name! Who does
that? God had given her such insight and great revelation about
the meaning of my name, Dorothy Hayes- God's Gift of Fire, and
the great exploits that would accompany my ministry. My other
unparalleled sister in the Gospel, Pastor T came and annihilated the
church when the Holy Spirit took away her notes and downloaded
the message, The Perfect Storm. I will never forget this teaching
and how she dissected that word! Finally it was Sunday afternoon
and my now big sis, Pastor Denise Baker was coming to preach
the house down! The afternoon was filled with such excitement
and anticipation! All I wanted and needed was more of God! Of
course I thought about Dorian and all that had occurred between
us, but I had to accept the bottom line; I was not ready for such a
contemplative man, and he needed more than I had to give. He's
an all around good guy and would move on to find the love that he

so desperately needed.

The church was packed and Pastor Denise never, ever disappoints when she steps into the pulpit. She came out the gate swinging and beat me all the way up! She was preaching about the ability to adjust to new circumstances and environments. God was doing something new and we need to relinquish our old ways of operation. Learn to adjust to doing things in a new, and even unfamiliar way. Submission to the process was necessary if we are to manifest the purposes of God. God requires us to be open to change. I was almost overwhelmed, and as she is preaching this message and breaking me down in the process, Pastor Dorian along with many members of his congregation walked in and joined the service. *"What is he doing here?"* I thought. I did not expect him to come today, and definitely not with his people. This is too much! I'm too open for this right now. Although I was happy to see Dorian and was grateful that he came to support me on my anniversary, I needed to focus on me! It may sound self-centered, but all of my previous relationships took me away from Me! DeeDee would lose herself, my standards would change, I found myself compromising, and I vowed not to ever return to that place again.

Pastor Denise was ministering directly to my soul and I couldn't help but to align her word to my experiences with Dorian. Was he the change I needed to submit to? Is he the new and unfamiliar in my life that I needed to get used to? As soon as she opened the altar, I came down front and center. I hit my knees and asked God to break me if necessary. If he was directing me to change my mindset, then please grant me the strength to submit to the process. After she prayed and I stopped crying profusely, I felt Joyce helping me up from the floor. Only it wasn't Joyce who grabbed my hand to lift me up, it was Dorian. He was standing beside me the entire time.

Everyone was now attempting to put themselves back together after hearing that powerful word from God. We had reached the point during service when acknowledgments were to go forth. Pastor T walked up to the podium and began to share with this afternoon's crowd what God had reminded her of concerning me. But wait. Before I continue, it is imperative that I stop to recount a few details about the weather that day. The skies were clear, partly sunny, and an overall beautiful day outside. Okay, back to Pastor T. She grabbed the microphone and reminded us of what God said, through her on Friday night. "Pastor DeeDee Hayes is The Perfect Storm." No sooner than those words left her lips, a huge bolt of thunder crashed down and shook the very foundation of the church! There was a moment of silence in the church. Then suddenly, complete pandemonium broke out! People began to shout, scream, holler, freeze, jump, I cried, and we ran and praised the Lord like we lost our minds. We could not believe what had just transpired! I believe a couple of saints were terrified and began to repent! This day, this weekend couldn't be more unbelievable. If I weren't there myself, I might not have believed this!

Normally only those listed on the program participate in giving acknowledgments and words of expression. But after that phenomenon, everybody wanted to speak! One friend of mine stood up and said, "I wasn't going to say anything, but I know that was God so I shall be obedient!" Today was just crazy and I was in a state of bewilderment at this point. Most of us were still standing in awe of God, and could barely bring ourselves to sit down. Then Dorian walked up and asked if he could have a few words. Everyone must have sat down, but I didn't.

He addressed the church in true Dorian fashion, with such poise and dignity, that he actually caused me to blush. While sharing his heart and love for me with everyone, he told of the night when he instantly decided to drive to another state, in the brisk snow, all because he wanted to make his baby happy. He then turned towards my mother and my step-dad and motioned them to receive their approval. "Approval of what?" I wondered. I was totally jacked-up by the day's events that I was literally confused. By this time, Pastor Denise had pulled my hand and nudged me to sit down. The only words I distinctly heard from Dorian were, "So if you will?" as he extended his hand towards me and leaned his head to the side. I was still attempting to process the words, "If you will?" I'm thinking, "If I will what?! What is this man talking about???" It finally dawned on me that Dorian was proposing to me!

The next thing I remember was Dorian hugging me, and I crying the ugly girl cry while nuzzling my face into his jacket. I had said yes. He eventually broke his embrace to speak to the crowd again. He declared, "To quote the famous words of Beyonce, if you like it then you need to put a ring on it." He reached into his suit pocket and out came a precious little black box. Suddenly everyone in the church rushed towards us as I removed my pretty pink butterfly ring, and he placed an exquisite and beautiful engagement ring onto my finger. People commenced to scream CONGRATULATIONS!!!!, cameras were flashing in our faces, and video footage was being captured. This was one of the best days of my life, and God had divinely orchestrated it all. He had to be in this! Who cues thunder and physically shakes a building at the same time? Duh?!

And we know that in all things God works for the good of those who love him, who have been called according to his purpose. -Romans 8:28 (NIV)

CHAPTER

"MONEY CONCERNS"

L et the planning begin! Everything was moving so fast! Too
fast! "Dorian take a minute and submit to reason. I need
you to just stop and listen to my thought process. We met
on January 17th, got engaged the last weekend of March, and now
we have a wedding date set for August 28th? You cannot in good
conscience, seriously tell me this relationship is not on steroids! I
refuse to believe that you would recommend, or be okay with this rate
of speed for any relationship you counseled," I pleaded.

"DeeDee, can you recall what Bishop Walters said to us during
our last marital counseling session? We spent six weeks of our lives
pouring out everything to him, and eight weeks to your pastors as well.
Everyone gave us the thumbs up!" he reminded me. Bishop Walters
even asked, "Why wait until August? After meeting with you both and

getting to know *you* better DeeDee, you two were obviously made for each other. I'm surprised you guys aren't already married," he said in amazement of our compatibility. Dorian ultimately convinced me for the final time, that this was the will of God for our lives, including the rate and rapid speed that this relationship was going. He had the ability and fortitude to talk me down off of the cliffs of life.

At one point during the planning of this extravagant ceremony, (this wedding was going to be my absolute last so I was going to have everything I've ever wanted!) I almost shut *everything down.* I was presented with another flag, but I closed my eyes, and moved forward with my blind man walking stick. You can call me Ray Charles at this stage. DeeDee once again began compromising her standards and I hated the way I felt about the decisions I was making.

On our first date, the dessert meeting, Dorian had offered to take me home. When he walked me to his car, I was happy to see he owned a very nice BMW. Two weeks later he purchased a newer model BMW, and that's great for him. This spoke volumes to me! What it said to me was, "This man is doing well for himself!" He has to have something in the bank in order to drive this expensive car, and to have the financial stability to purchase another one as he pleased was even better. He lived in one of the most expensive high-rises in White Plains New York. (I would discover later on in the relationship.) "Yes!" We appear to be on the same level financially or he is much stronger than I financially, and that is perfect for me too! Finally!!! One thing I do not have to worry about this time around. So I thought.

Dorian was *technically* unemployed during the planning stages of this wedding, and this fact served me a *huge* curveball. I promised myself that I would never be the breadwinner in a relationship again. *This wedding was not going to fall on my shoulders alone.* I need you to understand that I am not a Gold-digger, nor am I bourgeois. But I decided after previously living through what I call 'unbalanced relationships, you know the ones where the woman's income is substantially greater than the man's, that I would never do it again. I am not dating, much less marrying any man who made less money than I did. But here I am again, faced with another dilemma.

Yes Dorian was a Pastor and that provided some income, but unless you have a large and thriving church community who has an understanding of the biblical principles of giving, and is committed to honoring the Lord with their finances, the chances of a person being adequately sustained by the congregation is minimal. The project consultant job was 'on-hold', and as a result, so were the payments to his bank account. Suspicious thoughts were present but I forced myself to believe in Dorian. I reminded myself of all the 'fine dining' experiences, the constant gifts and flowers. *Dorian must be disciplined with his money to afford courting me in this manner.* I often asked if the project had resumed, and what time frame had he been given concerning the resuming of the job. Dorian was currently consulting on a project to rebuild a church in his hometown city of White Plains N.Y. We actually visited the worksite one day and his eyes filled with passion as he described the new facility. Dorian introduced me to the Pastor of the church and he raved on and on about Dorian's incredible work ethic and his vision for the revitalized edifice. (Okay, so another person is vouching for his character...Noted)

When we initially discussed our incomes, Dorian's was making about $85,000 a year to my $89,000, which was fine for me. I didn't view that as a substantial difference in salaries. Also, his church congregation was larger than mine, which meant he more than likely received a higher salary than I. He said the church was never consistent in the amount they gave, and as a result, the pay varied. I would ask for a number, any number, so I could at least know what we would be working with, but he could never remember any exact amounts. (FLAGS!!!)

At the onset, I had no genuine concern regarding the delayed project. His business and financial affairs were just that; his. Dorian's livelihood at the time were not of any concern to me, but that was before we were engaged and now planning a wedding; with one income. MINE. This new issue compelled me to revisit old scenarios…

"Babe this is our money. When we put your income and mine together, we can live a very comfortable lifestyle," I responded when the discussion of finances arose.

"But I'm not comfortable with my lady bringing home more bacon than I am at the moment. A man is supposed to be the head of household," would generally be his response.

"You are still the head of household and together we will make wise decisions for the house. But what do you suggest? Do I quit my job in order for you to be the bread-winner?" I would ask. *"Of course not; we need two incomes in this day and age. I just don't like it,"* would usually follow next.

"Then we need to decide what is going to happen because this is our reality right now as it pertains to the money. We have to straighten this out and come to an agreement. We can't continue to repeat the same conversation again and again," I now frustratingly stated.

"Babe I'm sorry, but as a man it just messes with my pride," usually followed next.

"Okay. If it helps, you can handle the money responsibilities," I

recommended.

"No, that's okay. I trust you to manage that. You're better with money than I am. I'll mess around and go out and spend it all," would be the response to end the conversation.

Everything would be fine and dandy, and A-Okay, until there was an issue that occurred with the money. As the manager of the funds, my job was to manage the funds. As said manager, I had to give a 'sorry no babe', or a 'not right now' as an answer to the consideration of a large purchase, or something we honestly didn't need. The conversation would quickly shift gears and I had a new title to add to my list. Controlling. "So just because you make the most money between the two of us, you get the final say on what we *do* with the money? I thought this was *our* money, DeeDee?" I now had to hear.

"It is *our* money, and you asked me to manage it, and not squander the money, honey." I would respond.

My position was this; buy whatever you want with your money, as long as the household money is utilized to sustain the house and the savings allotments we both agreed upon are secured. Many times I found myself in the position to have to hold down the household responsibilities, and their personal expenses too.

One husband wanted me to cosign for and make the down

payment on the purchase a brand new BMW. He owned his car, and it was paid off, but he wanted a new one because his was getting old. I said no, and that started a war in our house. If it's evident that you handle your finances in an irresponsible way, why would I agree, whether I made more money or not, to a decision for you to mismanage money even further? He had already begun to demonstrate that he was irresponsible with his purchases. There was a lack of responsibility with him paying any of his personal bills on time, or at all for that matter. And now I'm supposed to put my name on such a large purchase when I know, because he had done it to me before, that more than likely he's going to flake on this responsibility too? Then I'll be left holding everything! I said no, and as a result, he categorized me as a horrible wife who didn't support her husband. She was now a control freak because she had the money and good credit to give but wouldn't do so. Let me add that she was also the only one expected to pay for the repair costs of a leaking roof. I was done and couldn't take anymore. You better grab some pots and pans baby and place them strategically on the living room floor because it's going to rain tonight!

I cannot be that girl again. I have sacrificed and held households down before and DeeDee got burned *each and every single time.* I have worked very hard and diligently to put myself in a financial place of stability, free from lack and worry.

I will not place myself in the position for this to ever happen to me again. We either both had to come with equal amounts to the table, or he needed to own the whole table!

My personal experiences have led me to believe that many men and women have become misaligned and out of order concerning marriage. Men need respect, and women need security. It is really that simple. Men need to be the head in all areas of marriage, and women should acquiesce to that order. Ladies please put your rocks down, and don't stone me just yet; allow me to share this quick lesson.

Men do not feel a sense of respect if they cannot provide for their households; point blank period. We as women crave security. Love, support, and finances provide us with security. A sense of knowing that everything is taken care of is as crucial for women, as respect and honor is for a man. Humans are innately wired this way and to go against it is unnatural. When women are the breadwinners and their security is threatened, it suddenly shifts from *our* money to *my* money. When the man hears this, it emasculates him and he goes on the hunt to find something; anything that reminds him that he is Still the Man. It should be another job, but it is oftentimes another woman.

Men will cheat for several other reasons, and we all know this, but this present- day common issue is one of those reasons. Many men will cheat with a woman who, in his eyes, needs him more than we do. They internalize that we don't need them because we hold the heavier weight with the finances. So off they go to find a woman who will *depend* on him to pay her bills, or any other costs that she could use assistance with at the time. It's a win/win situation. This fulfills his need of being needed and respected, and in turn she now has security in knowing her needs will be met. Ask Mary J., Jill Scott, Wendy Williams, or Me for that matter. Many of you will argue and proclaim, "Not in my household!" Okay. Every household is different and when both parties are completely on one accord maybe it can work for them. It never has for me, so I am going to stick with my theory. My rant is done, but just because it's not expressed in your household, doesn't mean it is not existing in your household. Remember, for the majority of people, any body is better than no body.

All of my current, old-fashioned thinking comes from a woman who was raised by a single mom, and was taught and trained to NEVER depend on a man. "If you want something in life then it is your responsibility to go after it. You don't wait around for some man to do it for you!" my mom almost scolded. My mother's stories of hardship were enough to frighten anyone into working at least three jobs simultaneously. And worked hard I did, and still do. I have always provided for myself and did not ever give that obligation to any other person. The day I decided that I wanted a new car I bought one. When I desired to have designer bags and clothes I went out and purchased them. If I wanted diamonds and pearls I went and got them too. *Come on thru here Prince!*

But seriously, both of my prior marriages, to two completely different men, both included that same conversation around money. And today it looks as if this same discussion is about to be had with Dorian!

And I settled. Why did I settle? Why do we settle ladies and gentlemen? Why is it so difficult for us to say no? Why is everyone else's agenda, issues, or mishaps, our responsibility to handle? Why is the value we give ourselves, far less than the value we place on others?

Dorian promised that as soon as the project resumed, we would split the cost of the wedding 50/50. He would repay his portion of the money that we were investing in our future. He paid for everything now; the dinners, the excursions, the outings, movies, day trips, so why would I believe any different for after the wedding?

During his previous marriage he worked on Wall Street for some time, and after the crash, Dorian used his brilliant mind to successfully navigate the corridors of the White Plains hospital. His careers afforded him the ability to purchase a sprawling five bedroom home, luxury vehicles for he and his wife, a pen collection worth thousands of dollars, and family vacations of a lifetime.

Dorian was indeed the breadwinner and he duly managed

the finances for his family. Insert a photo of the Cosby's...haha...
needless to say, the family lived well.   As you can imagine Dorian,
was quite uncomfortable with our arrangement, but constantly
reassured me that lack of money would never be an issue we'd
have to face. He was willing, but more importantly, determined
to do whatever was necessary to provide me the lifestyle to which
I had grown accustomed.   It was to his honor and responsibility
as a man, to care for me and to cover me in every aspect of this
marriage.   My belief and trust in him was vital to his wellbeing,
I did believe, and I did trust. I love a man who readily fights for
what he believes in, and I am here to fight with you; even if we ever
did fall on hard times. But there's no one to fight with when you
are in the ring of life.... alone.

CHAPTER ELEVEN

"MARRIED LIFE"

$25,000. That was the ticket price of our exquisite romantic evening wedding. The reception, my gowns, his ring, the car, the church, flowers, gifts, the cake, the rehearsal dinner, singers, musicians, entertainment, floating lanterns on the beach, hotel rooms, bells, whistles, and everything in between, cost us a little more than $25,000. It was one of the most romantic and beautiful weddings I had ever seen! I can recall each and every detail and it was worth every single dime. The love, the prayers, the entire night was breathtaking and spectacular! When it was all said and done, I was especially pleased that although the cost was exuberant, we incurred no significant amount of debt. This is why I am adamant about securing multiple streams of income. We were still able to have money for the down payment of our first home together, which we were now in search of, so...full steam ahead!

As my pastors had so poignantly remarked during one of our pre-marital counseling sessions, the first year of marriage will already present challenges because two separate people are slowly becoming one. This will take time and patience. But Dorian and I were beginning our marriage with circumstances that could present protests in even the strongest of unions.

The first challenging dynamic was that Dorian's elderly and physically challenged mother lived with him, well now us, and we are her primary caretakers.   I was fine with the arrangement and was hopeful that I could now help Dorian with the care of his mother. He often complained that his free time was limited, he could never get a complete night's rest, and he was very uncomfortable caring for her private needs as her son. I completely understood, and as his wife I looked forward to being his helpmeet!

The second dynamic was my commute. The drive to work and church was a little more than an hour each way. We agreed, before the wedding, that I would move to New York while we searched for a home in New Jersey. He asked where I preferred to live and my answer was firm, I was a Jersey girl. He was fine with living in NJ and I made sure to narrow our search down to an area that would be in equal distance for the both of us. A thirty minute commute for him to church, and about the same distance in travel for me for work. An hour commute may not seem like much of a big deal for some, but when you have to rise at 4:00am to be on the road by 5:15am, late night rendezvous can present a problem.

Another vital concern was Dorian's children. His relationship had been strained with the kids since his divorce, but reconciliation with his son had begun to materialize. We needed to also be sensitive to his daughter's adjustment of her dad's new wife. The information given to me was as follows: "My son and I are speaking more frequently and our bond is being re-established. I wanted to give you a head's up that he may pop in and sleep over from time to time whenever he is in town." "Of course Dorian! This is your house and that is your son," I said. I would never hinder your relationship with your kids. "No DeeDee, this is our home and you must be considered as well. Besides, you are the lady of the house now. A happy wife equals a happy life correct?" he said as he smiled and walked away.

I was aware of all these circumstances before we were married. My goal was to come up with a plan for everything. I wanted to hopefully alleviate many of the obstacles that could arise. "Let's be proactive instead of reactive," I told Dorian.

I didn't want to leave any stone unturned. If we had a good plan in place, execution would be as smooth as humanly possible. Family discussions and counseling should be implemented as soon as possible. I will shadow you with your mom so I can learn what to do, and help her when you're not around. And as long as I am in the bed by 9:30-10:00pm, I am good as gold. I can get by, for a short time, on six hours of sleep. Surely, nothing went as planned. The worst part about everything was, it looked like Dorian himself was the saboteur!

Our marriage was absolutely incredible for the first month or so, but then I started to wonder if I was secretly starring in an episode of the television show 'Punked'. "What in the world is going on?" I puzzlingly asked myself. I felt like I lived in the Twilight Zone and each episode was stranger than the last! We were good while in the public eye; actually great! Everyone thought we had a wonderful and loving marriage. I honestly did too; most of the time. All of his friends and family, and even his parishioners applauded the wonderful job that I must've been doing as his wife.

*"Thank you for being so good for him. He is a totally different man since you've been around"

*"I'm glad to finally see him happy again; I've missed that smile"

*"Oh he loves you so much Pastor DeeDee," one home aide commented. "He talks to you for hours on the phone and I've been here for years! He's never been on the phone like that! Never"

*"*Whatever you are doing Pastor, keep on doing it! I love to see him like this.*"*

These words of thanksgiving and more, were the euphoric chatter of those who knew him long before I did, so what was this confusion happening between Dorian and I behind the scenes? I shortly came to realize that I had not been married solely to Dorian, but I was also in a union with his two fraternal twin cousins; Dr. Jekyll and Mr. Hyde. I would learn how to smile with him in public for the show, but in private, the channels of this marriage series drastically changed.

Our home life was already becoming seriously stressful, and Dorian morphed into someone who became unrecognizable. I was constantly being criticized for my failure to comply with yet another one of his needs, and as far as he was concerned, I, as a wife, was missing the mark. We were in marital counseling during the first three months of our marriage! Not a check-in, a 'how are you guys doing session, but a full blown 'something is gravely wrong with us' counseling session.

We were on the clock today so we had to choose our issues wisely. They were numerous so we narrowed it down to only a couple. We had major issues with our parenting styles. His children were pleasant towards me, but my irritation arose with how they treated him! There was either none, or very limited amounts of respect given to their father.

"Why does the current state of my relationship with my kids bother you so much DeeDee?" he asked.

"They are disrespectful towards you and this house. Your daughter speaks to you any ole way she wants to. She tells you to shut-up. What is that? When you call her phone, the phone you pay for, she only answers when she wants something from you, but if not, she ignores you and that is not right Dorian. I don't like it. *You* even complain about it, but when I suggest a conversation, you cower back. Why do you do that? Whenev….."

"She is a little girl DeeDee!" Dorian said as he abruptly cut me off; mid sentence.

This was another tactic that was often used in our conversations.

"She has been traumatized by the demented antics and negative persuasions of her mother. She is fragile and requires compassion. My daughter will soon adjust. The degree of communication and levels I choose to engage them, are my choices; not yours," Dorian said firmly.

"Is it my turn again, or are you going to continue to cut me off while I am speaking?" I asked visibly upset.

"You can speak now," he arrogantly responded.

Dorian was not completely honest with me about the living arrangements with his son. I was told whenever he was in town doing a gig or having a rehearsal, that he might stop by and stay over.

"That was not the truth," I told them.

"Dorian why didn't you tell DeeDee that your son was going to be staying with you two?" my first lady inquired.

"He does not actually live with us," Dorian replied.

"He is there practically every night Dorian. I feel like I was blindsided. When I wake up to go to the bathroom, you stop me and ask me to put on a robe because your son is out there on the couch. And if I can be candid, and this may seem insignificant, but I'm trying to have a spicy sex life. You always stop us in the middle of making love to go back into the bedroom because your son may walk through the door at any moment. I've waited a long time to have sex and now I can't be free in my own home!" I added. *Had I known this beforehand I would have been mentally prepared.*

"DeeDee you are self-centered and immature. He is my son and he will always be welcomed in my home," he responded sternly.

"And she is now your wife and she comes first," my pastor and first lady stated.

"Dorian, my issue is not with your son, it's with his father not telling me the whole truth," I calmly explained. They both agreed that Dorian should have disclosed the truth about his son staying with us. He did not like that.

They both also agreed that it was Dorian's responsibility, and not mine, to communicate the new house rules and arrangements. He as their father needed to have a discussion with them about his new life with his new wife.

I had been constantly cleaning up the house behind his son. I'd ask Dorian several times to speak to him about his hair all over the shower, in the sink, and on the floor, but he refused to. Dorian said the nature of their relationship was still very fragile and he wanted to prevent any further hostilities.

"Dorian he is twenty-two years old; not ten. He throws his clothes on the living room floor, behind the couch, and in the chair. I don't want to see a big pile of clothes every time I open the bedroom door. I'm not accustomed to living like that. I have to move his belongings just to sit on the couch. Besides my husband, I am not cleaning up after another grown man!" I quipped.

"Why won't you talk to him instead of attempting to throw me under the bus? I asked.

One morning, after talking to Dorian again about this nasty bathroom, he walked up to his son while I was standing right there in the kitchen (mind you the house is only about 800 sq. feet, so I'm practically standing in his son's face) and says, "I'm getting in trouble about the bathroom being dirty. Please clean it up so I can get out of the dog house," he laughed.

"Why would you say that Dorian?" I embarrassingly asked.

"It's true right? I told you I would clean it, but you insisted he does so I told him," he casually responded.

"No problem. Go on and let your children do whatever they want, Eli." I retorted.

"DeeDee you called him Eli!" my first lady shrieked. "You don't really believe that do you?" she asked. "That is not a nice thing to say to your husband DeeDee! Apologize to him," she rebuked. (Side-note: Eli is a king in the bible who let his kids run amuck. You can read about it in first Samuel☺)

My pastor and first lady did agree that his children were old enough to sit down and have these necessary conversations with us. The children, regardless of their ages must see you two as a united front, not divided. They will play you against one another and it's already happening. You put your marriage first, then, everyone else follows. Including the kids. The family discussions never took place....

Also during this session, I shared how Dorian constantly has issues with me. I expected us to have a couple of kinks along the road, but not so many and definitely not so soon! My God, I was not ready for this! If I had 3 issues, he had twenty-nine! And in only three months? We are still learning each other, and this will most likely take at least the next two to three years. I think Dorian's expectations of what he hoped this marriage would be, was unreasonable. His expectations of me were unattainable. He behaves as if all of a sudden I became this super busy woman who didn't make any time for him. I discovered while at a party with Dorian with many of his church members and friends, that before we married, he was a long time member of a bowling league. His friends were clowning him about being whipped by his wife. And as a result, bowling was no longer an option. When we left the party I questioned him about this. "I didn't know you were on a league! When was this and why did you stop? I asked.

"I stopped because of you," he answered.

"Because of me? I didn't even know about a bowling league Dorian. Why would you stop participating in activities because of me? You definitely should go back!" I strongly suggested.

"I stopped because I am now married," Dorian said.

I believe he expected me to do the same; Dorian expected me to stop my life because he was in it.

When he had problems or concerns with anyone else in his life; his ex-wife, his kids, the leaders at his church, or his ministry buddies, he took these issues to the Lord in prayer. But this same grace and mercy was never extended towards his new bride. She got bombarded with an onslaught of recommendations about what she either should have done in a situation, or how she was to respond the next time one presented itself. If I were to give an example of every grievance he had with me, this book would easily supersede the bible in length. But I will share only a couple of his complaints of my short-comings.

"DeeDee is constantly on her phone. Every time I turn around she is texting or talking to someone else," he stated.

"Dorian, my phone usage hasn't changed one iota from the moment you met me. I'm living the same exact life that I was when you entered it. I pastor a church, I am building a business, and I did have friends before we met. But I do intentionally refrain from using my phone when we are spending quality time together. So what's the problem? Besides, your fingers hit the buttons on your device just as much as mine do, but I have never said a word to you," I responded.

"It's too much DeeDee!" he barked. "Honey is it unreasonable to desire my wife's complete, and undivided attention every now and again?" he then softly asked. I quickly glanced at my first lady, and then caught the eyes of my pastor as if to ask, *"Did y'all see that? Did you just see two totally different people just now?"* I think they missed it.

"Sure Dorian, no problem. I will be mindful of my excessive phone usage while in your presence, your highness" I sarcastically replied.

"DeeDee that is not nice," my first lady corrected me. "You need to apologize," she motioned. (Insert a deep breath here.)

"I apologize Dorian."

121

Why am I always the one apologizing. Now I have to walk around like a freaking kid trying to hurry up and end all phone communications when he is around. This is great, smh...big sigh.

The session wrapped up with them asking how I was handling all the new adjustments. Moving into a previously established home, living in a new state, helping out with his mom, navigating the new neighborhood, the longer commute in that relentless N.Y. traffic, and now attending two services every Sunday. Dorian wanted me by his side in ministry, so I now attended, and ministered at both his morning, and my afternoon worship services. (Dorian only attended one.)

Dorian felt slighted and was offended that the question was only posed to me. He told them he also has experienced major changes since we've been married. "What changes Dorian? Dresser drawers and closet space?" Those are your major changes? The landscape of my *entire life* has changed! Please tell me how the focus of everything always ends up back on you?" I clamored.

I explained to them, as I had already done with Dorian, that it in no way feels like my house. There were so many things I was not prepared for, and now I feel like a stranger in my own home. Dorian reassured me that this was no longer solely his dwelling, but ours together. I was not in agreement with that statement.

I could not be the lady of the house because I had no idea what happened there. I would get ready to cook, but someone was already in the kitchen cooking so I would have to wait. I'd prepare to do our laundry, but the machines were already in use, or the detergent bottle was empty. This is your house and I just live here with you.

One evening after work, I was in the kitchen cooking dinner and I heard someone coming through the front door! I had recently talked to Dorian on the phone and he was at church. Veronica, my new friend and mom's health care provider, was in the room watching The Word Network with her, and it was much too early in the night for his son to be home. I was nervous so I grabbed the butcher knife out of the sink. My heart raced as I waited in the kitchen for the culprit to appear. I have watched too many horror movies where they search for the killer only to end up dead, so I chose to wait. To my amazement his sister walks around the corner and we both jumped in surprise at seeing one another. I was not made aware that his sister also had a key to the apartment. She had come to drop off food, snacks, and some toiletries for mom. Earlier in our courting stages, Dorian informed me that he was the only responsible sibling who helped with his mother's care. Obviously that wasn't true either.

"Dorian, the workings of your household are normal to you, but they are new to DeeDee. Can you make her aware of the daily routines, the aides and their schedules, and all the things that have been previously established in the home? As a woman, she has an innate need to run her household, but she is hesitant to step into that position because it's already filled," my first lady asked.

"I can attend to that," Dorian replied. They were not aware, but because I was learning Dorian, and it was clear that he was irritated with the direction of this session.

"And as for my mother," Dorian immediately chimed in, "DeeDee no longer assists with her at night. She disagrees with my methods of care, and mentioned her lack of sleep, so she opted out," he blatantly lied!

"You have got to be kidding me Dorian! That is a bold-faced lie!" I shouted. "You know I do not care that my pastors are sitting here, and they know me. That is not true at all! You didn't want my help so I backed off and left yall to yourselves. This is what happened, Pastor!"

When Dorian's mom calls our phone in the middle of the night, I tell him to stay in bed, and I go to her bedroom to help her. Dorian demonstrated for me, no less than ten times, what I was to do to assist her, but suddenly here he comes rushing in the room after about 5 minutes, as if to rescue her from my incompetence. "I thought you needed a break Dorian? You said you were going to be so excited to have help, and now you could experience an uninterrupted night's sleep? I am trying to help you baby so why do you insist on coming in the room if I'm already here with her? If you keep it up, she is never going to get used to me," I opposed.

"My mother wants *me* to help her. She has made mention

of this," he replied.

"But mom will have no choice but to accept *my* help if you stay in the bedroom. I mentioned to her that you are asleep and getting rest, but then I look like a fool when you come bolting through the door like Superman!" I said.

"Look we have tried for a few weeks now and she is not adjusting well to the change. She rarely does well with any sort of change. She is this way with the aides, doctors…practically everybody. She is my mother, and she only wants *my* help at night. I will resume the majority of her care when the aides are not present," he said.

"Your mom is playing you Dorian. We get along just fine during the day when I spend time with her. I help her out even when the aides *are* here. Some days we *all* talk and have a good time together. But Okay Dorian, you got it sir. You can go back to saving the day. I'm going back to bed. It's one o'clock in the morning and I have to be at work in a few hours. Makes no sense for us both to be awake, " I moaned.

"You actually sat here and tried to paint a distorted picture of me?" I questioned. "You are off the chain Dorian. I don't understand you."

Both of you guys have to be more patient with each other. Rome wasn't built in a day, and neither will a well-oiled and refined marriage. Give each other some mercy and a whole bunch of grace. You two love each other dearly, so make every effort to extend that love to one another.

When we left the session, I was under the impression that we were going to be okay, but it was only a matter of time before he was to yet again, find fault with me.

Dorian was a light sleeper. When I awakened at 4:00am to prepare for the day, he would usually go into the kitchen to pack my lunch bag, and then he'd walk me to my car.

"DeeDee, we need to have a conversation about what transpired the other day in the car. I know we discussed this already, but I discern there are deeper areas of exploration that we have yet to touch."

"Oh my Goddddddddd! Oh my Lorddddddddd Doriannnn! Can we talk about this later? I have to go to work," I whined.

"This is exactly what I've been discerning. Every single thing in your life takes precedents over my needs and cares," he said.

"Work Dorian? I am going to work. You are so needy! I have to go to bed early in order to wake up for work at 4 o'clock in the morning, be on the road, leave by 5:15 AM. I then drive, almost half sleep, for an hour to go to work! I then teach my beautiful, crazy kids and make sure that they don't kill each other all day. After work, I'm usually in meetings and on phone calls in attempts to grow our businesses. We have committed to attaining multiple streams of income. We are about to invest in a home. We both said we desired to live debt-free, and none of this will happen by osmosis Dorian. Then after all of that is said and done, I have to drive another hour back home, cook dinner for you, and be the sex kitten that you so love and desire. And I do it all with a smile on my face. And I am happy to do it. It is called sacrifice. It is what we do in a marriage, but nothing ever is enough for you!" I said holding back my tears.

"What you are expressing to me is because you go to work every day, that a job is more important than my needs and wants?" he bickered back.

"No I'm not saying that, but until you do find a job, I am the only source of income for this household. The businesses are not stable enough to completely sustain our lifestyles yet, and neither are the stipends and offerings we receive from church. Let's forget about the future, what about our now Dorian? If I don't go to work and instead, take off to explore your emotions everyday, how do you suppose we will buy groceries, pay the car notes, car insurance, this high behind rent, our cell phone bills and whatever else we pay? It's not going to happen if I'm in La La Land 24 seven 365 days a year with your feelings!" I shouted.

"DeeDee, I need you to hear me. I am emotionally collapsing," Dorian said.

"*You* are collapsing? I can barely stand Dorian! I am gaining weight, you have issues with me rising early in the morning to go to the gym, but when I come home I have to prepare you dinner and get ready for tomorrow. Then you say I'll cook. But you cook the foods that I can't eat! I explain over and over that I can't do lots of pasta and I never use butter; but what do you cook? Shrimp scampi with pasta!" I exclaimed.

"What woman doesn't want her man to cook for her? Another woman would be grateful!

And another thing DeeDee. I am very annoyed that you can will yourself to awaken at 4:15am to go to the gym, but you request that I discontinue waking you up for sex in the middle of the night. I have no control over when my desires arise. You are always the most important factor in this relationship, DeeDee!" he replied as if he were brutally offended.

"Dorian, you twist everything I say! I have never once denied you. I asked you to be cognizant of my schedule. Sex every night is fine as long as we can start no later than 10:00pm. It's called compromise, but I am the only one to use this wonderful marital strategy that you constantly remind me to implement!" I yelled.

"First of all; stop cutting me off when I am speaking. If this relationship continues down this road I will start to implode. When I implode I shut down. When I shut down I go into my own thoughts and that is not a good place for me to go; it is not a safe place. It behooves you to allow me to express my thoughts and needs, or I will shut down. I can feel the process beginning. This happened with my first wife, and it's about to happen with you," Dorian threatened. "I have asked you repeatedly to not compare me, or this marriage to your first one."

"Shut down? We have only been married for six months and you are shutting down? You know what Dorian, I feel like we've been married for twenty-five years! But it's only been six, long, drawn out months. Sex, sex, and more sex Dorian! That is all we are supposed to be doing right now as newlyweds. Just having hot, butt-naked crazy sex!! All the time!"

I thought we would still be in the laying up under each other, eating and sleeping, and then waking back up to have more sex phase. But we're not! All we do is argue; like old people!

"I am attempting to create moments of happiness, and remarkable memories to last us a lifetime DeeDee, but you are continuously otherwise engaged with all things but Dorian," he responded.

"This is about that bird isn't it? We are going through all of this early in the morning because of a stupid bird?!" I screamed.

"It wasn't a stupid bird DeeDee. It was an opportunity to witness the soaring of a rare eagle in flight, and you missed it because you were on your phone!" he yelled.

"Well nigga, you should've missed it too because you were

the one driving the car!" I busted out laughing.

"Do not try to make me laugh DeeDee, I am very serious right now," Dorian said.

"I'm not trying to make you laugh Dorian. I'm trying to make you see how crazy this is. We've only been married for six months Dorian. We have the rest of our lives to create wonderful memories. And we have created a few amazing memories so far. We've gone horseback riding, bowling, and we've seen all the movies you've ever wanted to see. We take long walks in the park, search out lakes to discover, go sightseeing, and all the other fun stuff you love to do outside. But time doesn't always lend itself to just creating memories; not during every waking moment of the day. We can't live in a fantasy world that only includes you and I," I explained.

"All I require and ask for is your support and your attention. You still spend considerably too much time on your phone. Joyce, church members, partners from the business, anyone warrants more time with you than me," he frustratingly expressed.

"Dorian, this is not fair! You want me to do everything with you and for you. How much attention do you need?" I asked.

"As much attention as a wife should give. I've mentioned that my neck has been hurting me, but you haven't done a thing! I give you massages all of the time! What about me?" he blurted out.

"What about you? It's always about you. I gave you a gift card that I received as a gift for me, but I gave it to you Dorian. I gave you my gift so that you could use it to go get a massage. And let's be very clear, boo. The only reason I get those massages from you is because that's your version of foreplay. It's not about *my* relaxation, *my* rejuvenation, or reducing my stress. Those are the reasons I used to go get massages, but remember you asked me to stop going to the spa; you wanted to massage me. But when *you* give a massage it's all about sex; it's about you!" I fussed.

"You go on YouTube to research everything else, so why not research and learn how to give your husband a massage?" he explained.

"You have got to be kidding me!" I shouted. *This is too much.*

"Dorian we seriously need to go back to counseling with my pastors because something is off. I cannot understand your way of thinking, and you obviously don't understand mine," I suggested.

"I'm not certain if we should continue counseling with your pastors. It's evident they are partial to *your* side," he pouted. "My pastors are partial to the side of RIGHT! They do not take sides Dorian and you know that. You just cannot fathom someone seeing your faults and knowing your deficiencies. You are not perfect Dorian so stop pretending. You agreed to go to counseling and your highfalutin Pastor refused to marry us, much less counsel us, and we need somebody; anybody at this point!

"My mother told me this morning that I am a good son. A GOOD SON DeeDee, yet you continue to find fault with me!" he shouted.

"What the heck is that?" I shouted. "I never said you weren't a good son Dorian! And that has nothing to do with what we are talking about. You being a good son doesn't mean you can't have other issues. There are several issues you find with me, but I know I'm a good person, daughter, and friend. One has nothing to do with the other. I'm beginning to understand why Georgia said you had mommy issues. We are wives, not your mother Dorian," I shouted back.

"I'm going to be honest with you DeeDee. I am seriously having second thoughts about this marriage. I am not happy at all, this is not what I signed up for, and massive changes are imperative to the survival of this relationship!" Dorian squawked.

"Second thoughts? What do you mean second thoughts? There *are no* second thoughts. We are married until death do us part! Do you remember the covenant we made *with* God, each other, and before our family and friends? I told you *before* I married you that I am never, ever getting another divorce. This is it buddy! So second thoughts or not, we're going to have to make this work," I firmly responded.

"I am beginning to escape into my headspace, and this is

not a safe place for me to be DeeDee," Dorian warned.

"Well then I'm going to have escape with you *into* your headspace, and then bring you back out of your headspace because wherever you go, I go; remember?" I reminded him.

"This is serious DeeDee! I believed we rushed into this marriage too soon. I've been contemplating. I've had thoughts of a divorce," he calmly responded.

"Ooh really Dorian? *We* rushed into marriage? And now you're thinking of divorce?"

"I don't know what we are going to do, but we have to make this work, because like I told you before, the only word in my vocabulary that starts with the letter d in regards to us, is death, as in until death do us part; not divorce. We promised that we would never get divorced regardless of what happens. We will forgive, we would scratch, scream, yell, and fight and claw our way back to each other in order to save this marriage, but we would never consider divorce so don't you ever say that to me again Dorian!" I screamed while crying.

"Okay DeeDee, I'm sorry. But in the heat of throws you've thrown around the option of divorce too," he reminded me.

"I know, but I apologized and said I would never say that again. I can't be dumb enough to curse my own marriage by speaking craziness into the atmosphere. You got me out here crying and I have to go to work," I fussed while wiping the tears from my face.

"It's okay to cry DeeDee; it's an expression of deep lament," he said. I just stared at Dorian in utter amazement and confusion. "Dorian, you are crazy. I am beginning to believe you do this stuff on purpose. I am convinced that you need to see a professional," I said with *all* seriousness. He laughed and said you're crazy too DeeDee. "We are just crazy about each other."

"No, no, no, no. I think you are trying to *drive* me crazy, but you are a certified nut case." I responded.

"Well you make me crazy too, DeeDee. I kicked over that garbage can back there because of my enragement. But then I did go back to pick it up, so maybe I am a little bit off," he laughed. Who does that? You can't even express anger like a normal person.

"Have a good day at work sweetheart," Dorian waved as I drove off.

Is this nigga serious? Have a good day at work? You can't give me all this business in the parking lot at 5:00am, then just switch up with have a good day at work. God, you are going to have to divinely intervene or something because this here is bona fide pyscho!!! Shoot, now I'm going to be late again!

> *Can two people walk together without agreeing on the direction?*
> *—Amos 3:3 NLT*

CHAPTER TWELVE

"THE FUNERAL"

S adly enough, I knew my dad's death was upon us. God had already spoken to me, and He was very clear. I notified Dorian that I needed to take the trip to Fredericksburg Virginia. I understood if he had to remain behind to care for his mom. Dorian did not like many outside people up in his house. There were offers extended from close friends to come in and help with mom from time to time. They suggested some occasional R&R for the newlyweds, but most of the time Dorian's answer was "No, thank you."

I called my sister and asked her to make amends with our father before he left this earth. She had to see if arrangements could be made for the kids. She did not take the trip. Dorian said the trip was too long for me to drive alone. Although I have driven Route 95 down to my dad's house several times before, I simply replied, "Okay Dorian."

Fourteen months and forty-five pounds later, marriage to this man had taken its weary toll on me. Endless days of arguments, hostile shouting matches, and heartbreaking silent nights were enough to censor any responses of objection from me. Our marriage had been depleting to my soul. I was losing myself; losing my voice. My throat was in tact and there were no raspy vocal cords. But I lost the voice one has when they just want to be heard. I figured if I didn't say anything, my words could no longer be twisted or misconstrued. This marriage was in a cautiously weakened state. Whenever I talked to God about us, it was with prayers that only He could understand. I had made every request imaginable and my feeble attempts at formulating words into new prayer appeals were unsuccessful.

Dorian and I were still intimate, and it was decent. Not once had I ever denied Dorian sex, but the naughty toys, lingerie, and high-heeled stilettos were now boxed up and hidden in the bottom corner of our bedroom closet.

We headed down south that same weekend and as usual, my father was the life of the party. He was forevermore the comedian; most of the time to the embarrassment of his sweet wife. My dad is where I get my sense of humor. He was a straight clown, but the last several years had been devastating to his body, and strenuous on his wife. Whenever I had a visit, at some point like clockwork, the routine was always the same. I first went into his little refrigerator that he kept in his bedroom, grabbed some snacks for us, crawled into the bed with him and the dog, and then we'd talk and laugh about whatever the topic was of the hour. He'd always end up joking, making fun of the men I chose. Daddy didn't care if he was my husband. Anyone who walked into that house was fair game, and I knew it. And then he started. He commenced to begin cracking jokes about Dorian and when he started, he didn't know how to stop! He said Dorian was a little man and that I'd better be careful not to break him into two pieces. I was a Hayes and we were built strong! "Daddy, you are a crazy mess," I laughed. " I know Dee! I knowwwwww ! Haaaaaaaa!!!!"

Dorian and I prayed with my father before we left to head back up the highway. I kissed my dad and promised that I would see him soon. At the time, I didn't realize how soon it would be.

When I married Dorian, the members of his church came up to me and asked what title they should use to address me. To know me is to understand my utter disdain for titles, and how they have been "produced" in the church. I am absolutely not beat for titles. My former pastor had to basically force me to allow people to address me as minister, so you can imagine how difficult it was for me to answer to pastor. Then when the realization came that I also carried the mantle of a prophet; you could just forget it. *God, I will prophesy but they don't need to do this title thing again.* I told them you are free to address me with whatever makes you comfortable.

But you are a Pastor, and now you are our first lady. Over some time, Pastor DeeDee was usually reserved for my congregation, and most of his members addressed me as first lady. Dorian would tell me they needed their first lady. For several years they only had a father, but they lacked in many areas because the nurture and care that a mother brings has been missing. Even during the times that he was married before, they still were void of a mother's love (according to Dorian). The sacrifice on my part was great, but I made the commitment to be there for them. Two services back to back; no breaks or reprieve in between. Traffic and more traffic. Speeding up and down the highway to honor the call on my life and to be the woman of God that I was called to be;

I would be there every Sunday morning to take that dreaded uncomfortable walk down the aisle as we entered the sanctuary together, hand in hand. Some would stop their praise and worship to smile, wave, or show any kind of acknowledgment. Dorian would wave back, smile, and tap an occasional shoulder as he strutted down the walkway. Dorian loved this; I on the other hand did not. I have my issues as it pertains to the rules, regulations, and traditions of the house of God.

During some portion of the service, usually the altar call, Dorian would extend his hand towards me, and motion for me to come up and join him. Together we ministered to the people of God, and the Glory of the Lord filled the place every single service and without fail, lives were forever impacted. Afterwards, we would make our way back down the aisle to greet everyone with hugs, kisses, love, and blessings. I loved his congregation but this first lady was not the best at being an actress. It slowly became unbearable to sit and watch this man deliver the word of God, when behind the scenes he was a completely different person. The "Sunday morning Dorian" was encouraging and full of grace and forgiveness for the people. The compassion and love extended toward the souls was beautiful. I have to assume that it all was poured out onto them, because once he walked through the doors of our home, he suddenly had nothing left to give. The "after 2:00pm Sunday afternoon Dorian" was emotionally distant and he constantly sat in the seat of judgment. All of the mercy and patience he afforded his congregation expired on Sundays after the hours of 11:00am- 2:00pm. Our relationship had gotten to the point where I no longer wanted to serve with him in ministry. I felt as if I were being used. In my mind, my own husband was pimping my anointing. I stopped attending his services as I was depleted, and running on empty. I had a congregation to feed and I was running low on nourishment. I loved his people, but I was assigned to my flock first, and his would need to depend on whatever the anointing was that he was carrying; or not.

Every year, Dorian's church hosted an annual bus ride to the Shopping Outlets to an all-you-can-eat buffet. This Saturday event also served as an opportunity to celebrate Dorian's birthday. Everyone sang Happy Birthday and celebrated another year of their Pastor's life. The all you can eat restaurant was the same place that Dorian said he submitted to that *once a year* steak splurge. The prime rib there was amazing though. Today, I can remember this bus ride as if were yesterday.

"First lady, we miss you!" I heard as I entered the bus. But today I sensed some tension coming from a couple of his members. The atmosphere was thick and I was downright uncomfortable. Maybe it was my subconscious playing tricks on me and making me feel bad, but when a few of them neglected to meet my eyes with theirs as they were greeting me, I knew then that some were upset with me. I did not want to be here, but I had no other service, speaking engagement, or business meetings to attend. I had no excuse to use to get out of this one. I felt so alone. Of course Dorian was there, but I was still alone. I wished someone from my church was with me. I felt like I owed every one any explanation as to why I had abandoned their church. Were they thinking that as a wife I was not supportive of my husband? How can the first lady of the church not attend her husband's services anymore? That is flat out disrespectful. She is out of order! She needs to play her position? She is never here anymore. How could she do that to our Pastor. These are the thoughts I believed they were having about me. Maybe I was over exaggerating a little. Suddenly, my ride or die crew called out to me and asked if I wanted to come to the back and sit with them.

Now because Dorian is the reserved, dignified, and (let's just call a spade a spade) the uptight corny one, he sat all the way in the front of the bus as I would learn he does every year of this trip. "Do we have to sit here in the first row? Do you want to move closer towards the middle or the back area?" I suggestively asked.

"No, I always sit in the front." He responded.

Of course you do. Now I on the other hand, am carefree, fun, and outgoing and I wanted to go to the back of the bus with the fun crowd. They were laughing, joking, and having lots of fun. Dorian *knew* I wanted to go back there. He watched me as I continued to turn around and smile at my people in the fun seats. He said that I could go back there with them if I wanted to and that he didn't mind. But we both knew that was a lie. If I strolled to the back of that bus, our car ride home was guaranteed to be filled with lectures, complaints, and instructions on why next time I was to remain in the front of the bus with him. Needless to say I stayed with Dorian and would try to make the best of the trip.

I had been in constant prayer for our marriage and was currently a few weeks into reading this book called *The Love Dare.* This is a 40-day Christian devotional designed to help strengthen marriages. Each day you are to read the scriptures and principles that were aligned to that day's devotion, and then execute the day's 'dare'. At the end of the day you are to journal your experience and chart your progress. I began to see some positive changes happening in our marriage and it felt really good. One night I found myself in the bottom of our closet pulling out our box of goodies. That was a very good night.

Sleep had taken over most of the people on the bus, including Dorian. My face pressed against the cold glass, and it was refreshing and soothing. I was looking out of the window at the beauty of God's creation and began to smile when I noticed the horses grazing in the fields. My instincts were to tap Dorian, but the distance between us was too far. "I *hated* the state of my marriage," I thought to myself. A few good days here and there weren't cutting it. I needed God to speak to me, so I decided to use the duration of this ride to talk to Him. I heard the Lord say, "Go see your father. He is going to die soon." I just sat there. That is not what I expected to hear from the Lord. I tapped Dorian on the arm and told him that I needed to go back to Virginia to see my dad. *You just saw him.* I know but I have to go back. God just said he's about to die.

"DeeDee I just started this new job. I can't take off to drive you down there," he reminded me.

"Dorian I've driven to Virginia by myself before. It's fine, I'm good," I said.

I immediately called my sister. "Hey lady. I'm going back to see daddy and you need to come with me. I just heard the Lord say that daddy is going to die soon," I said.

"Why would you say that? DeeDee don't say that!" she whined.

"I know what I heard Karin. You need to bring the kids down to go see him. He's never met his granddaughter and he hasn't seen his grandson in years. I'm leaving this week so the kids will miss a few days of school," I said.

"Okay I'll go," she responded.

By the time we arrived dad wasn't doing well at all. He began to cry when we walked through the door of his room. His face lit up like a Christmas tree when he saw his grandbaby. He was so weak and frail. My father was no longer the 6'4 boisterous, loud and strong man that I knew. I forced my tears back and talked to my dad about Jesus. My father *believed* in Jesus, but his actions were oftentimes contrary. Every time he landed back in the hospital I would tell him to get his life together. He would say I know Dee, I know. He would joke and say if I end up in hell I know I'll be there with a lot of my friends.

Bible in one hand and my dad's slender hand in the other, I led my father in the reading of the sinner's prayer. I anointed him with oil and prayed for the grace and mercy of God to surround him. Four days later, he was gone.

My sister and the kids drove down with me a few days before the funeral so we could help our stepmom with the planning process. Dorian would drive down the night before the funeral and after he left work. He had been kind and comforting towards me. I was fine, and my sister seemed pretty okay. My concern was for my stepmom. She had done everything in her power to create a happy home for my dad. She really loved that man and at times, I questioned how she did it for all these years. I told you my dad could be a handful.

We gathered daddy's clothes, shoes, watches, collectibles and all the gadgets his money could buy. Ana, my dad's wife, wanted to donate his clothes and she gave my sister and I all of his jewelry. I asked Dorian if we could give my dad's clothes and shoes to some of the less fortunate in his church community. He agreed and I began to pack up everything in my dad's closet. Ana yelled upstairs to warn me to be very careful. She said my father's guns were hidden somewhere up in that closet. My father was a retired police lieutenant and for as long as I could remember he kept two guns in the house at all times. None of us ever knew where he kept them. Ana and Karin were too scary, and he thought that I was just too crazy to know. After removing my dad's custom-made football jerseys from the pile of clothes that were going to be donated, and after dividing them up between Karin and myself, I grabbed the step stool so I could reach the top of the closet to get down his cowboy hat collection. *DeeDee was keeping some of these for herself!* I started trying on his fancy hats and under hat number four were my father's two guns. He had a revolver and a semi-automatic. I told Ana when I found the guns and she told me to keep them in the closet. She didn't want to see them. We agreed to take them to the police station after the funeral.

Dorian arrived late in the middle of the night and I was grateful to have him there. I was emotional that day and tonight I needed the embrace of my husband. Earlier in the day, I had written a letter to my father. Before his body went into the ground, I had to release the deep pain and hurt caused by my dad's absence. When my parents divorced I was only one. I only saw my dad on the weekends. Some of those weekends were missed, many arguments between us were had, and a few years of my life were completely void of his presence. My father didn't meet my son until he was the age of three. We had some war-like battles, but I loved my daddy and in time I would always find myself back in his refrigerator, eating his snacks, and laying up under him laughing and cracking jokes.

I knew Dorian had to be tired from the long drive down, but because we promised to never deny one another, I knew I could count on his comfort tonight. It would be the last time I made love to my husband.

Family and friends came from far and near to pay their respects to my dad. During the service, before the casket was closed, I put the letter in my father's suit pocket. I told God that I was also burying any resentment, hurt, and grudges that I held towards Dorian. I loved Dorian and I promised to do whatever was needed to keep us together. The funeral service was beautiful and the burial was one of honor. Ana was presented with my dad's flag, as the accompanying military soldiers played Taps. As the family was settling back into the car, my sister, Ana, and I were still in tears. One of the soldiers gently knocked on the window to get Ana's attention. Ana was given a piece of paper that contained the location of my dad's plot. She asked me to write it down in the event that I came to the cemetery to visit my dad. I didn't have a pen, so Dorian pulled out his iPhone, and reached across me to take a picture of the information for me.

If anyone owns an iPhone, more than likely you are aware of the text message privacy features. If a text message comes through and your notifications are not set to private, the beginning portion of that message, or the complete message if it is not a lengthy one, is visible and displayed. As a new iPhone user, Dorian was not aware of this feature.

Poobaby Campbell
I LOVE YOU BABE!

This is the infamous message that flashed across the screen of Dorian's new work iPhone. I rapidly blinked my eyes to ensure that the tears falling from them were not skewing my vision. **"I love you babe?"** **"PC?"** I had several conversations going on in my head in the span of thirty seconds, my brain was going a mile a minute!

"Okay DeeDee, you know what you just saw. Do not pretend that

you did not just read a message come across your husband's phone that said **"I love you babe."**

"What do I do right now???

"Do I say something, or act like I never saw it?

"No you dummy!! I just told you we aren't doing that anymore!! I refuse to be that First Lady of the church who has to handle the hoes politely!"

"God, you know me!!!!" "I'm about to lose it in this car; limo driver and all! I don't care who is in here! My mother always said, "Where you act up, is where you get dealt with! I have to deal with Dorian now!"

"DeeDee calm down, you are saved now! You are a Pastor of a church now. Your niece and nephew are in this car too! You will wait until you both get back to New York.

Maybe I'll hire a private investigator to follow him when I get back ."

"My stepmother will have a nervous breakdown at this point if I go off." "Why is she in this car????" "Okay. Calm down DeeDee; she can't handle anything else right now."

"But if I wait, I'm not honoring myself! I have been losing myself to this man! What about me? I have to stand up for myself!

"Why am I so hot?!" "Is it supposed to be this hot in October?" "It's so hot in here!" "No, I can't wait!!!"

"Dorian I just saw a message come through your phone that said, "I love you babe!" Dorian who is texting you?" I asked.

"What? I didn't see a message on my phone," he quickly lied.

"Yes Dorian, a message just came to your phone; I saw it." I said.

"No it didn't," he snapped.

"Dorian I swear to God! Stop lying!" I heatedly whispered.

"Who is texting you I love you babe?! Who is Poobaby?....
Oh my God! Portia?! Portia is texting you?" I bombarded Dorian
with a slew of questions.

"I don't know why she texted that!" he squirmed. "I
thought you just said no message came through on your phone!
Let me see that phone Dorian," I commanded.

"No." he stuttered.

"What did you just say to me? No?! There is no 'No!' "We
don't ever say No! We have never said 'No' to one another; about
anything! What's mine is yours and what's yours is mine remember
Mr. Communication! Mr. Sharing is pivitol! There is no 'No' with
us! Dorian give me the phone!" I quietly demanded while clenching
my teeth and moving closer towards him.

Dorian took the phone and immediately put it in his back
pocket. "It's private, and lower your voice DeeDee," he quietly
said.

"Dorian, I swear to God! I swear to God! I swear to God!
I swear to Godddd!!! If you are cheating on meeeee!?" I cried.
This is not happening right now. I just buried my father and this
can not be my life right now. Then I broke down.

We are taught to give people the benefit of the doubt, that

they are innocent until proven guilty. I believe in seeing the good in everyone. I am optimistic about life, people, and becoming our best selves. But I have learned that when the Holy Spirit speaks, He *only* speaks the truth. He Cannot Lie! God reveals, uncovers, and exposes! When He does, and He will, you better believe Him; point blank period!

DeeDee, how in the world do hear everything else that God is saying, but deny His voice when he shouts to you about relationships? What is your issue and why do you force yourself to believe the best in people who you know aren't right? The circumstances of this situation had to be orchestrated by God. I am not the woman who checks or even desires to go through her man's phone or personal belongings. If I have a need to do all of that, then I shouldn't be with you in the first place. You could not have paid me to believe that Dorian was cheating on me, but I can't deny what I saw and his refusing to let me see the phone confirms it. My heart is telling me he is lying. In my mind, I know he is lying. God you have been showing me signs all along the way and I can't continue to turn a blind eye to this one. Dorian is lying to me, and he is not the man I wanted to believe he portrayed himself to be.

"Come on Dorian!!!" I thought. You pursued me like none other; you chased me down and pulled out every bell and whistle to prove your love for me, and now I have to discover, on the day of my daddy's funeral that you are nothing but a bold-faced, deceitful liar? After all of these valiant efforts to win my heart, his constant chasing to wear me down, and the lavishing of chivalry and adoration; It was nothing but a game to him?

My face flooded with tears and I could feel my heart beginning to dissipate...Again. Oh NO God wait! Please stop this; I can literally feel my heart beginning to break! The pain is returning, again! I know this depth of hurt all too well. We've had intimate relationships with each other in the past, and I've promised Pain she was banned forever, and would never be allowed to return to my heart again. The lacerations that accompany this level of agony require too much time to properly heal. I won't survive this one God. I have too much scar tissue from previous relationships. This was my last time remember?

My legs began to shake. I started to rock back and forth as if I were a deranged person in an insane asylum. I began to mindlessly stare, directly into Dorian's pitiful big brown eyes; I didn't speak a word or utter one single sound, but I just stared at him in his face. Dorian looked like a lost deer caught in headlights. My eyes were fixated on the man who took an oath before our family and friends; the Pastor who took an oath before the church and God; the knight in shining armor who took an oath before me to honor our marital covenant above any other person on this earth and he... told... me... No. Everyone knows when a man refuses to give you his phone he is cheating. No evidence required.

"You lying bastard," I said. "You are disgusting to me. Why can't I see the phone Dorian?" I asked.

"This is not the time or place, DeeDee. You need to calm down. We will view the text message together at the house," he promised.

"I'm about to lose it in this car!" I thought. I can't wait to get to no house! Wait! I could use this car situation to my advantage. My sister is crazy as a bag of nuts and I know exactly how to set her straight off! She spent a couple of days in jail for throwing t.v.'s and knives at negros! I can count on her! All I have to do is say the word and she will pounce on him like a wild cat; then I can go get that phone out of his pocket!" I decided. Yup, let's do this Karin!!!

"DeeDee, I know you miss your father girl," Ana said interrupting my master plan.

"Here, it's alright to cry. Take some tissue. At least we know he is in heaven and there is no more pain," Ana said while wiping her face with her Kleenex. "Ugggggggggg....WHY is she in this car???"

The car ride back to my father's house was nauseating. I could see him thinking. He was trying to figure out what he was going to do. When the car pulled up in front of the house, everyone had already arrived. The repast was scheduled to be at the house, so now I have to walk into a house full of family and friends. There were my dad's beautiful neighbors on the porch standing and awaiting our arrival. "How sweet! I'm gonna need y'all to go back in the house because ya girl is liable to bust!" I thought while grasping onto Dorian's arm and waist. Once we got out of the car, Dorian said he needed to go to the trunk of his car to grab something. No problem sir; we will be taking *this walk* to your car together. I was not giving him any opportunity to step away from me for even one second! He thinks he's going to delete that text. No sir! No you will not! I held onto him like white on rice. Everyone thought we were so cute together, and that he was holding me up; supporting his wife through such an ordeal. The right side of my body did not part from the left side of his. We were so close together, stuck like glue today. Absolutely not; this Negro was not leaving my side!

We walked into the house and everyone was saying hello and embracing us. I told them that we needed to go upstairs for a moment because I was distraught. Dorian had never walked so slow in his entire life; he's usually quick like a little jackrabbit the way he runs around. But not today. He was trying to take his sweet little time getting up those stairs. Dorian had some trouble walking up the spiral section of the staircase because of my attachment to him. We were secured, arm in arm, and my other hand was grabbing onto the front of his pants. Once into the bedroom, we sat down together side-by-side on the bed. I took a huge deep breath, and prepared myself for the worst. I knew that I would have to focus and deal with whatever was on that screen. While sitting there Dorian leaned over to get the phone out of his pocket. As he began to open up the message, he suddenly stood up and backed up towards the television away from me so that I could not see the phone. Well when he moved, I moved. I popped up and jumped directly in front of him. "Really! What are you trying to do Dorian? Open up the text," I ordered him.

Dorian pressed the button on the phone and swiped left! He attempted to delete the message! When I saw that red delete sign pop up, my right hand responded before my brain kicked in; almost like it had a mind of its own! The next thing I know, I had smacked Dorian so hard that he fell back into the t.v. and hit the wall. He grabbed the phone and put it back in his pocket and then began to rebuke me for smacking him.

"How dare you?" he shouted. "No woman has ever put her hands on me. I have never in my life been smacked in my face. How dare you put your hands on me DeeDee!" he responded awaiting for my apology.

"You can't stand here and tell me that Georgia never smacked you. As crazy as you said she is? If I'm smacking you within two years of our marriage, I know she must've smacked the mess out of you in twenty!" Give me that phone Dorian!" I yelled.

"No DeeDee I will not give you the phone! How dare you

put your hands on my face!" he repeated.

"Stop making excuses! You are lying and you're hiding something! I cannot believe you're doing this to me. After everything I've been through with you! My stupid self putting up with your cuckoo behind for almost 2 years and you are lying to me? Why can't I see the phone?" I urged.

"Because it is private. I do counseling sessions often times on my phone, and I have been helping people with their personal situations. You are not privy to these conversations DeeDee. They are confidential," he spewed.

"I don't care if you are Barack and I am Michele. There could be a secret service mission happening involving the United States of America and if a situation arose between them that had the potential to destroy their marriage, Barack is giving that phone to Michele!' I responded sarcastically.

"I do counseling and the information that others share with me is held in the strictest of confidence," he arrogantly responded.

"Dorian, why is Portia texting you I love you babe? What kind of counseling have you been doing with her?" I asked.

"I don't know, maybe she is grateful because I have been counseling her daughter and helping her to get back on track with life.

"Counseling her daughter? Since when have you been counseling anybody? And if you were her child's esteemed counselor, how come I didn't know about it?" I said.

"I wasn't certain of your response to Portia's request. I believed you would be unwilling to allow me to minister to that family. They have been through an excruciating ordeal with the loss of Portia's eldest child," he responded.

"Cut the bull Dorian, I can see all through you right now. You are good," I laughed.

"See there, I knew you would object. So yes DeeDee, I held that secret from you, the one and only secret," he said.

"You are a liar. Give me the phone Dorian. I love you babe is not an inappropriate response to relay thanks to you for a counseling session," I quipped.

"No DeeDee, you will not be allowed to search through my phone. I am a pastor, and one of a pastor's job is to keep and hold all matters of his flock in complete discretion," he pompously responded.

"I'm a pastor too Dorian and if I know that something has come between my marriage that could potentially destroy it, I would disclose whatever information was needed to save my marriage," I responded in desperation.

"Well I'm a *real* pastor DeeDee and it works differently for me," he exclaimed.

"A real pastor? Are you trying to insinuate that I'm not a real pastor? Why is that? Is it because you have 15 more members than I do, that I'm not a real pastor? Maybe I don't suck up to people like you do in hopes to get ahead or make connections. Or is it because I refuse to conform to certain traditions, rules, and regulations of the traditional church that I'm not a real pastor? I'll put my small church up against yours any day! There is something called OIL at my church. We have the hand of God at my church. The anointing flows heavily within our church community. I've had one of your church members stop me outside after your service and he asked me to please come every Sunday. "It's not the same when you're not here First Lady; it's just not! Please stay First Lady."

"I promise you that my congregation significantly shows change over the course of years after being at my church. They actually *read* their bibles, and whole-heartedly try to apply the principles of God to their lives. There is this little thing called *fruit* that my members often display. After the way you complain to me about your members and how they act, can you say the same? You done pissed me off Dorian!" I screamed.

"You are arrogant, pompous, and completely full of pride Dorian. Just because you have a need to display your expansive vocabulary, and wear your little old raggedy suits twenty-four hours a day, doesn't make me less of a pastor because I can rock jeans and still flow in the supernatural power of God in my ministry. So is that why you and your cohorts constantly barrage me with questions and requests for our churches to merge? Did you gentlemen think I wasn't good enough to pastor? Or like you all would say, it just makes sense to combine the two? You probably wanted to combine the churches because you would finally have an anointing in your church! Man, I am so glad that I didn't listen to you," I responded.

"Whatever DeeDee, I'm not addressing that; it doesn't matter. I am appalled that you struck me. I need to go, I need to get on the road." Dorian said.

"Go? Where do you think you are going? No you're not going anywhere! We're going to see this phone and settle this." I said.

"No we are not. We will reestablish trust and renew the distorted areas of our marriage." He replied as if everything were normal. "We will have to go to counseling or some other form of mediation because my phone is off-limits."

"I told you that I did not want to get married again because I couldn't ever again face the possibilities of a divorce. And I'm supposed to allow you to tell me anything you want and I just blindly believe you after this mess? You must have lost your mind! You don't even look like yourself right now Dorian. I can't believe this is happening to me. I fell to the floor and began to sob. Are we getting a divorce? I told you I was never getting a divorce again, but I can't live with someone who keeps secrets from me. I know you are lying!" I sobbed.

"We will have to reestablish trust. Stop crying, it's going to be OK. I need to gather my things because I need to get on the road."

"Are you serious Dorian? You are going to leave right now?"

"I think we need some time apart to think. Now give me a hug," he commanded as he tried to embrace me.

"Don't touch me, get your hands away from me!" I demanded.

"Now what if I get on the road and have an accident or something like that? You would feel horrible wouldn't you?" he asked me.

"Please get away from me!" I said pushing him off of me. Dorian's face looked weirdly distorted and he actually started to really scare me.

Dorian collected his things and made trips back and forth to pack the car and head back to New York. He told me to get the clothes and shoes from my dad's closet and he promised to give them to those in the community at his church. I wiped my face and tried to get myself together, but I was enraged!

"This bastard is going to just leave me here like this? Like I am some chic in the street and not his freaking wife that he made a covenant with before God!?"

I could not stop crying! "He'd rather protect some

witchcraft practicing whore over his wife! Do you know what I've sacrificed to be with this mediocre frame of a man? Nigga I held you down financially for two years and put up with your overly sensitive Ralph Tresvant ass and you put this hoe before me?!"

Rage, heartache, betrayal, disgust, and an indescribable sense of loathing came over me!

"Get it together DeeDee!" I told myself. Honestly, my tear-stained face blended right in with everyone else's, so if I was caught still crying it made sense to automatically think it was because of my dad. I walked into my father's closet and started to grab the bags of clothes and shoes to give away to Dorian. When I reached up to grab a bag of hanging suits, I remembered my daddy's guns. Maybe I found those guns yesterday for a reason. "Those guns have been hidden from me since I was a little girl, and *I'm* the one who just happens to find them yesterday? I think this is a sign and you know what Dorian?" I thought. "If this is going to be *over*, then it's going to be *all the way* over. Where is that gun?!" I said reaching up for the semi-automatic. Thanks Daddy; you finally came through for your baby.

I hurried back into the bedroom, sat down on the bed, and put the gun under a towel so that he couldn't see it when he came into the room. When he walked into the room I asked Dorian one last time if I could see the phone. He denied me access, so I snatched the gun and backed up on the side of the bed and pointed the gun in his face. "Nigga, I told you I wasn't getting another divorce. So you have a decision to make here and right now. Which one of us is going to go, Me or you? Because the way I see it, I don't feel like living right now, and you no longer deserve to," I explained.

Dorian looked like he was going to pee on himself.

"DeeDee, put down the gun," he said oh so softly.

"No boo. You won't show me your phone, so I'm not putting down the gun," I protested.

"DeeDee, you are being unreasonable and I need you to calm down baby," he said.

"Don't try and sweet talk me now! I see you for who you really are, you liar!" I replied. "Everything is going to work out fine. We will go to counseling, whatever you want to do. We will make this work. Now please, I need you to put down that gun," he tried to persuade me.

"No Dorian. One of us is not leaving this room because I have had it up to here with y'all lying niggas! I cannot handle another affair. I have always been faithful! To you; to everybody! I have never cheated and I have had opportunities to do so! I should have cheated!!!! I cooked, I cleaned, I screwed your brains out, and this is what you do to me? I told you in the beginning that I can't stand liars, and that I don't do secrets. My heart hurts, and I am officially done. So, you need to choose. Is it going to be you or me," I asked while alternating the barrel of the gun between my head and his.

"DeeDee, I do not want anything to happen and I would be devastated if either one of us was to get hurt. How would we explain that?" he asked.

"You are garbage Dorian. You're only concerned about appearances, but don't you worry. I already notified Joyce and my pastors of the situation. I told them that I'm going to go get my daddy's gun, and that one of us may not make it out of here alive. And I informed them of the reason why, because I know your lying ass would fabricate some phony story to make you look good. So in case anything happens to me; my people already know the truth. The text message has been sent." I explained.

Dorian suddenly lunged at me to grab the gun. He put his finger behind the trigger to stop me from pulling it. He is so excessively dramatic. So now his finger is cut up because the trigger is hard metal and I was already holding the gun with the firm grasp. He jerked the gun away and began to rebuke me. He told me how crazy I was and how I put his life in imminent danger. I must be a lunatic to put a gun to his face. I jeopardized his position as a father, a pastor, and a caretaker for his mother. "You are going to regret this DeeDee!" he threatened.

"Whatever Dorian, give it a break. The real you is out now so stop pretending," I thought to myself. Dorian barely spent real quality time with his family, and as far as I'm concerned now, he's nothing more to me than a false prophet.

After he finished packing up the car, Dorian came back into the house and gave me the gun. I no longer needed it. He was dead to me at that moment and the events of the day had taken its toll. He got into his car and drove off to head back to New York. I went upstairs and put the gun back in my daddy's closet. I decided to pray, but I couldn't talk to God at that moment. What would I say? I got up and decided to answer my cousin's summons of me to come and join the family downstairs.

The company and long lost family members had finally dispersed after helping to clean the house, and ensuring that Ana was okay for the night. My sister and I dragged ourselves up the stairs and resigned to my guest bedroom. She wanted to sleep in the bed with me tonight. We climbed in the bed as I unpacked my computer. Regardless of how I felt, I needed to be in God's presence more than anything else. There was a sermon by T.D. Jakes that my home-girl Pam sent me last week and she promised that this word was a life changer. Every, and each time I attempted to view it I became distracted, or preoccupied with another issue or someone else's agenda. It was quiet, and my sister and I were in a state of reflection, so I felt it was the perfect time to watch it. 'Blinded by Rage' was the title of his message. There are no adequate words or eloquent verbiage appropriate enough to describe what happened to me as a result of this sermon; God is real y'all! He promised to never leave us or forsake us. He was with me the entire time of this marriage, and of this day. This word from God served as the genesis of my process of restoration.

> *People with understanding control their anger; a hot temper shows great foolishness. - Proverbs 14:29 (NLT)*

CHAPTER THIRTEEN

"THE SABBATICAL"

After the gun fiasco, Dorian left for New York but continued to call my phone; excessively. He said that I was mentally unstable and he wanted to check on me to make sure that I had not harmed myself. "Like you actually care Dorian," I thought. We argued back-and-forth on the phone for hours. He told me not to come to our home in New York but to spend some time at my mother's house. How dare he tell me that I cannot come to my own home? "You've been staying there a couple nights a week because of the excessive commute so you will be fine," Dorian directed. "Wow! I see it now! You didn't suggest that I stay at my mom's house a few days a week because I was falling asleep behind the wheel almost everyday; you wanted me to be in Jersey so that you could run around with Portia. This is crazy! It's all beginning to make sense now Dorian," I replied. "Crazy? I'm not the one who pulled out a gun DeeDee! You require psychological help," he snapped.

"That's alright Dorian. Keep avoiding the topic and God will just continue revealing the truth! Bishop Walker told you in counseling that God would reveal anything that you do wrong; and He most definitely is," I replied.

When I got back home to New Jersey, I told Joyce and Pam everything that went down. Pam had been dealing with some similar issues with her husband, and she suggested that we take a much-needed vacation. She was absolutely right; we needed to get away; far, far away. "Let's go to the Bahamas!" she suggested.

"I've been everywhere *but* the Bahamas so yes; we should go!" I said excitedly. "We're going to the Bahamas, we're going to the beach, and we're going to God!"

I reached out to Dorian to get his permission to go to the Bahamas. Why am I reaching out to this fool? I asked myself. Didn't he tell me not to come home, so as far as I'm concerned he doesn't have to know where I am going. But here we go again; The Holy Spirit telling me that I have to honor God in my marriage. I called my lying husband and asked him if I could go away to the Bahamas with Pam for a few days. Dorian, without any hesitation or deep thought, said yes. He believed the trip was a good idea because we needed some time apart. And I bet he also needed to make some adjustments with his girlfriend Portia.

Off to the Bahamas we went! We stayed at the Cove in The Atlantis Hotel. If we were going to go, then we decided to GO BIG! Favor followed us throughout our entire getaway! This departure was truly ordained by God himself! If Pam and I do nothing else, we always end up in prayer and in praise. Neither one of us is too loud for the other, or can praise for too long. This is what we do! So much so that we actually ended up praying with the housekeepers that worked on our floor of the hotel. The beautiful ladies would hear us in the room praising the Lord throughout the days and nights of our reprieve. One morning we received a knock on our hotel door. Pam had already made the beds and chased down one of our ladies for extra towels and soap, so what was this knock for? It did get pretty intense this morning in prayer so we initially thought we were in trouble. We figured they'd warn us to be quiet. The Cove is the most expensive section of The Atlantis and we assumed we'd offended a few guests that did not share in our enthusiasm for Praise and Worship every day! Instead of telling us to quiet down, they asked if they could join us. My Joyce eyebrow rose and Pam looked at me as if to say, "I don't know if they are right in their spirit pastor?" I whispered to Pam that if I sensed anything ungodly they are out of here! We have had our fair share of fake church folk. But these ladies were the real deal!

They shared how they would listen to us praying in the

morning and knew that we were anointed women of God. They even called in one of their friends who was off from work that week to come in and meet us. She was the 'prayer warrior' of the trio. We prayed heaven down in that room you hear me! What an encounter! God's presence was so strong in the room that I began to feel guilty. "God do you know what I just did to my husband? I know he is wrong, but that doesn't mean that I am not. And today you grant me the pleasure of engaging in such an awesome experience in you? I wondered in awe. We prayed, we praised, and 'The Prayer Warrior" in their click prophesied over our lives. Absolutely incredible!

Please tell me, what two women end up going to church with their local island cab driver that just happens to be a deacon in his church? I was set on attending a church I knew of in Nassau, but when Pam asked our driver about the distance, he recommended his own house of worship. Mr. Raymond listened to gospel music whenever he arrived to take us to another site on the island, but we had no idea that he was a deacon in his church. Not only did Mr. Raymond suggest a church for us, but he also promised to pick us up! Although we know the people say to come as you are, we also knew our beach attire was not going to cut it! Remember, our reasons for coming to the Bahamas was not for a girl's trip, but to be restored and revived in the habitation of God. Needless to say, we decided to purchase a few beautiful and fancy sundresses for the service at church.

Bright and early Sunday morning, we prepared ourselves. Worship couldn't come fast enough for us. We almost ran downstairs to meet Mr. Raymond. Mr. Raymond and his wife pulled up to the hotel promptly at 9:00am, and Pam and I suddenly felt extremely uncomfortable. Our gorgeous flowing summertime dresses, immediately appeared like innapropiate nightclub attire compared to Mr. Raymond and his wife's Sunday's best. Shimmery stockings, shiny suits and brooches, and a huge hat accompanied Mrs. Raymond's garb. I looked at Pam and decided that our seats today shall be near the *back* of the sanctuary. This is their church and obviously this choice of fashion is apart of their culture, so we must respect that.

My plan was drastically foiled as Mr. Raymond informed the pastor that Pam and I were his special guests, and were visiting the island from New Jersey. The pastor and his wife then called us up to the altar to pray over our lives and for our safe journey back home. "Oh Lord Jesus!" I hesitated. "I surely do not want to get up in this sanctuary to the meeting of the side-eye stares of these people, " I thought to myself. We took the long-road walk down the aisle and of course there were noticeable cackles and rolled-eyes peering over our choice of dress, but we got over it. Since we're here we may as well receive these prayers and be on our way.

Toward the ending of their service, apparently the custom of the pastor and his wife is to walk the sanctuary and greet the parishioners. When the pastor approached us, we attempted to quickly gather ourselves after hearing such a powerful word of God. My face was saturated in tears. I told the pastor of our prayer encounter from the previous night. Everything he preached was exactly, almost verbatim, the word of the Lord released and revealed to us while in prayer at the hotel. He smiled at me, and Mr. Raymond told him that I was a pastor. He overheard Pam talking to me in the car. When she talks to me she always calls me pastor, and not DeeDee. The pastor then *informed* me that I was to address the congregation with a few words. "Oh no sir, no thank you sir. God bless you, but I'm fine pastor," I nervously responded. When he returned to the pulpit to give the benediction, he made an announcement that the service was coming to a close, but there was a word of the Lord to be given. He declared to the congregation that there was a prophet in the house, and he motioned me up to the pulpit. "Come on God!" I whined. "Not right now," I said while slowly dragging myself up the stairs to the podium. At this very and exact moment, I remembered a dream from the first night of our arrival. This is the dream.

I was very upset. I had arrived at my preaching assignment, but my 'church clothes' were M.I.A. I did not have my preaching attire and felt I couldn't effectively minister to the people. I didn't think they would receive me because of my casual attire. . I was in a traditional church that needed new wine. "Jesus! My God!," I thought.

God, this can't be happening to me right now. I'm hardly dressed appropriately for this church, and my mind is in a state of discombobulation. *I* left the country so I could be poured *in to* remember. I'm on a sabbatical Lord! Besides, what 'word of the Lord' are they going to readily receive from me? I shared the portion of my dream that I now realized was specifically for this house. After, I began to prophesy and was on the brink of really going in, but church house etiquette reminded me to 'hold my mule' as they say. The next thing I know, the pastor admonished the people of God to come and bless the prophet. A line began to form and the people, one by one flocked to the front of the church to come and sow seeds of blessings into my life. They placed money in the basket, tightly embraced me, and then, the Holy Spirit wanted to show off! "God are you serious?" He came through there like a rushing wind! I began to prophesy to everybody in the line. When I came up for air, the line had gotten even longer. Pam came to assist me in praying, and the pastor assigned a few of his leaders to stay with us until God was finished.

This church conducts two services every Sunday, so the man of God departed into their fellowship hall to have breakfast in between the two services.

The line eventually came to an end. We left the sanctuary

area and were escorted to the fellowship hall where breakfast was still being served. Delicious plates of food were set aside for Pam and I. Space was reserved for us at the Pastor's table along with his wife, Mr. Raymond and a few other ministry leaders. While eating her fruit for breakfast, Pam looked at me in what appeared to be amazement, and I shook my head, returning the sentiment. I think we were both still in shock.

Today was unbelievable! Was this real? It's a challenge to fully comprehend the events that are transpiring at this moment in my life. I couldn't comprehend going through such pain, and God allowing me to still operate in my calling; in my purpose. "Wasn't I wrong though God? *I* pulled a gun on my husband and you sent me to a church across the country to prophesy your divine word? They received an offering for me! These people do not know me from a can of paint! I have never been to the Bahamas a day in my life! God what is going on?" I puzzlingly asked. God replied, "They know *me*; and *I,* know you."

Once we returned back to the hotel, we decided that it was a perfect time to go for a long walk on the beach and bask even more in the presence of God. Pam and I desperately sought the voice of God and complete solace during this harsh season of our lives. Pam roamed on one side of the beach, and I strolled alongside on the other. As I walked in the warm sand and prayed for almost an hour, I clearly heard the Lord say, "Dorian has filed for divorce."

I stood there, frozen. I felt the wind of God gently sweep across my face, and my feet were planted in the shallow end of the water. "Okay God. What do I do?" I calmly asked. "Do I fight for my marriage, or do I sign away on the dotted line?" I wondered, fully submitted to His will for my life. I walked down into the water until it reached above my knees. I was on a journey back to peace and that alone became my purpose. I took this peaceful moment to reflect. In each marriage, I was faced with dishonesty, betrayal of my trust, and deceitful acts. I was now, just, tired. None of these men deserved my unwavering commitment, willingness to sacrifice, or a love that outlasted eternity. But God did. I had a choice to make. I decided to stay and fight for this marriage. Regardless of what *Dorian* chose to do from this point on, *I* was fully submitted to God concerning Dorian and the marital vows that I had taken. My focus was God; and He would take care of Dorian.

I honored my covenant with God, and the vows 'for worse' are still the vows I meant. I walked back to shore with a strong resolve that I was becoming a better version of myself. I will be still and know that you are God. Change me, deliver me, and set me free to be at peace with whatever the outcome of this circumstance will be.

After my glorious time in The Bahamas, the following Sunday, I returned to church and addressed my congregation. I explained the details that I felt were appropriate to share about the events that took place at my father's funeral. For several reasons, I chose *not* to mention Dorian. A few of my members would have taken a trip to the Bronx immediately following service if I had. Pastors must know their flocks.

"Some events took place that I am not proud of, and although I am graced with God's forgiveness, it is also my responsibility to hold myself accountable in the same areas that I hold you accountable. I honor my calling as the shepherd of this body of believers. It is to be upheld with all reverence to God, respect and seriousness towards you. In the same manner of selectiveness I use for allowing other preachers in this pulpit to ensure that you guys are in good hands, I utilize for myself. I am sitting myself down for a month and allowing the other very capable and anointed ministers of the house to facilitate all church services," I explained. They were responsible for every Sunday service, as well as any and all mid week gatherings. For those of you who may be unfamiliar with this practice, it simply means I *publicly* acknowledged my sins or shortcomings, and relinquished my rights, or the charge to lead the church. I required time to grant God full access to my soul and spirit without interruption of responsibility. While making this serious and solemn announcement to my church, my beautiful mother, in only a way that she can, yelled out in the middle of the service, "No! You don't have to sit yourself down! I don't know what happened in Virginia, but I know your father's crazy family. Somebody probably said something to piss you off and you went off and let'em have it!" She explained to the congregation.

"Mommy, I'm going to need you to calm down. We are still in church," I replied while shaking my head. "I bet you I know who it was, too!" she mumbled.

"This is my life, church; this is my life," I laughed.

Our trip served as a launching pad into wholeness for the both of us, and the restoration of my soul was in full process. I returned to New Jersey and prepared to go home to my new reality, but Dorian informed me that I was not allowed in the house anymore. "You should be ashamed of yourself, DeeDee! Your immaturity supersedes your decision making process. How dare you take a luxurious vacation while our marriage hangs in the balance?" he criticized.

"Am I going crazy, Dorian? You gave me your permission to go! I honestly could have gone and you not know anything, but I still asked your permission. You never called me anyway so what does it matter? You agreed the time apart was best," I replied.

"Your mother's house should have served as the location destination for our time apart. Not some inappropriate girl's soiree while you and another woman slept in the same bed on some remote island!" he declared.

"Dorian! Have you really lost your mind? Why are you insinuating pure ridiculousness? Of course we slept in separate beds. What is the problem?" I asked.

"I no longer trust you, DeeDee. Your actions are unpredictable," Dorian exclaimed. His reasoning for not allowing me back home was pure Dorian antics. He said his safety, and the wellbeing of his family would be comprised and I was not to return under any circumstances.

" You can't bar me from my home Dorian," I explained.

"I just did. The locks are changed and your remote key device will be deactivated next week," he said.

"Wow. What a man of God you are Dorian; what a man."

After a few days, Dorian suggested that we meet to sit and talk. We met at a diner in New Jersey; the same diner where we met for dessert. When Dorian walked to the table I barely recognized him. His face was drastically different. There appeared to be two people that now shared his body. He ordered our food and after the waitress walked away, Dorian told me that he filed for divorce yesterday. I told him I already knew. He asked how. I just looked at him and asked how do you think? He knew I heard from the Lord on deep levels and I think it actually bothered him at times to know the close relationship I maintained with our God. I told him that I was going to fight for our marriage; I wasn't going to give up. Dorian simply responded there was no point in fighting. His mind was made, and like his first marriage to Georgia, once he makes up his mind, he was finished.

"You gave Georgia 21 years and I can't get two?" I asked. "Why waste any more time if we know it's not working. I won't do another 20 years and have it end in the same way," he said. I simply said okay and continued to eat my food. He attempted to start an argument like he had done many times throughout our marriage, but this time I didn't take the bait. I had to recognize and stop falling for the tricks of the enemy.

Throughout the days we would text, but we barely talked. I decided that he cannot just kick me out of our home! I paid half of the rent, I started paying for the cable, and all of the groceries were on my tab as well. How dare he? So one Monday evening, as cool as a cucumber, I let Dorian know that I was coming to get a few of my belongings. He attended classes on Monday nights at his bishop's church; well at least he stated he was currently enrolled in class on Monday nights. At this stage I had no clue what was true or not. He usually came in very late after class so he arranged for someone to be there to let me in the house. Can you imagine the embarrassment of having to ring the doorbell to your own home? I was met at the door by his cousin. We were cool, but he was there to stay, watch, and escort me back out when I was finished getting my things. I told his cousin that I was staying. He called Dorian.

While in our bedroom I initially laid down to take a nap, but I heard God speak twice. He said 'Search'. So I searched. I found a card from Portia, and several letters and emails from Georgia located under his socks in his top dresser drawer. Dorian spoke of Georgia with pure disgust; he was certain of Portia's insanity so why would he keep their letters and cards? Why collect memorabilia from people that you no longer wish to remember? When you greatly dislike someone you discard everything that remotely reminds of you that person. In one of the letters from Georgia, she was apologizing for striking him across the face. Once again, another lie exposed. *I thought I was the first woman to ever hit you boo?* I also found a speech that was written for his congregation, but I would never know if he actually gave it. The speech was addressing his church in regards to his divorce from Georgia. It started with the phrase, "There is no other woman, and there is no other man. I have made all attempts to save our marriage but blah blah blah."

Why make this statement? Irreconcilable differences are just that; why elude to adultery? Why 'suggest' that she could have been the one cheating? So this dude must have cheated on her too! The other letters I found from Georgia, and the one card from Portia were all cries of sorrow and apologies. These former lovers were both deeply saddened by their emotional reactions and the pain they've caused Dorian. They both similarly admitted to their bouts of immaturity and having a lack of sensitivity to his needs and feelings. "Oh my God in heaven!" I proclaimed. This is Dorian's M. O.! "God what does all of this mean?" I asked. "Keep revealing Lord. I'm listening."

When Dorian arrived home he walked into the bedroom and saw me sitting on the floor. He commanded me to leave the house. I was again disobeying his requests. I announced that he had no right to kick me out of our home. He threatened to call the police if I refused to leave. I suggested that he make the call. I believed God for the restoration of my marriage, but I was tired of being bullied. He called one of the deacons from his church over to the house to 'talk some sense into me.' I submitted to a conversation with him and we talked for close to an hour. He convinced me that Dorian was adamant regarding my departure, and if I were to submit to his request, he may eventually soften to mine. The deacon helped me to carry most of my belongings, he walked me to my car, and I returned to New Jersey that same night.

This time around, I took a leave of absence from life. I went away for two weeks and locked myself in a hotel room. Joyce was the only person who knew of my whereabouts. During these two weeks God changed my life forever.

Days one and two were devoted to sleeping and crying. I submitted to the pain, and ceased from trying to force myself out of the bed. My body rejected the command to rise; my heart denied the charge to mend; and my mind shunned the embracing of a new reality. The beginning of day three was impelled more by my hunger than my own will. I grabbed a banana to eat and hit the floor to pray. While praying I saw the face of a woman I have been following on Periscope. Pastor Sarah A. Morgan. The Lord instructed me to go watch her teachings on Periscope. I dragged myself to my computer, set up the Wi-Fi, and took out my notebook. I typed her name into the search bar and clicked on her last video. As she spoke, my heart started beating uncontrollably; I experienced what was equivalent to heart palpitations. The beautiful angel from heaven was teaching on the spirit of manipulation. While watching her, I began to have flashbacks of Dorian! Every conversation, his weird actions, those confusing responses, sudden lapses in memory; so that's what this was? I began to scream my head off in that hotel room! I thought I was going crazy! "This man has been manipulating me the entire time of our relationship! How could I be so stupid?" I shouted. I had no idea! I was oblivious to this spirit; well at least to the broad degree of it all.

Dorian has several stories about his childhood and A Lifetime Movie couldn't do it adequate justice. His narratives were exceeded by heartbreak. Dorian recounted details of his past with such vibrancy. He captured emotions to the point that you felt as if you were there. It all made sense now. Dorian easily remembered specific details about events that occurred when he was seven, eight, and nine years old. He shared how he failed to receive the same levels of love and attention that his siblings did. He recalled how his mom and dad solely focused on the church and other business ventures and he was neglected; severely neglected. Since he, and only he was the responsible child of the four, he was forced to grow up faster than the other children, and had numerous responsibilities that they did not. Dorian would find himself gravitating to one of his uncles in the family in an attempt to get the love and attention he so desperately craved.

This 50-year-old man was attempting to manipulate me into giving him what he believes he never received as a child; Or at least that's what he thinks. *God, This is so good!* My mind is on fire now! The Holy Spirit is speaking!

During one disagreement, Dorian accused Georgia of being heartless. She told him he had mommy issues, but she wasn't his mother; she was his wife. And she was right! *Oh Georgia you should have talked to me.* Georgia, me, or even that witch Portia can't make you whole; only God can! I cannot believe this. How did I not know about this, God? Why was I never taught this! Everyone needs to know this! Pastor Morgan was breaking this thing all-the-way down! Out of a list of maybe fifteen different categories to be cautious and aware of, Dorian fit the bill for close to nine of them. I understand now! Oh my good God in heaven! I felt so excited and relieved at the same time. I was not crazy! DeeDee is NOT crazy! DeeDee is being manipulated!

This is only a small portion of what I've learned from Pastor Sarah A. Morgan's teachings on manipulation. Thank you woman of God!!! Thank you God for directing me to this understanding!!!

Manipulation is a spirit of witchcraft. When you refuse to adhere to the manipulation spirit, it gets frustrated, aggravated, and agitated. The person will behave like a child; they then plot and scheme and do evil.

They become very upset when things don't go their way. They believe their world is falling apart. Then they make you feel that your world will fall apart without them.

The controlling spirit of manipulation operates through people. They manipulate people, events, and situations to go their way. They spend hours trying to figure out how to get you to do what they want you to do. They think a lot. They will sit and think, but not share, because you can't know what they are thinking. You cannot interrupt their thoughts.

They must be in control; have to be in charge. Nothing is right without their input and direction. They must give their two cents. Their way is the only way possible and the best way. They want to have the power of your decisions, and of your responses. They argue, they whine, they make excuses, they procrastinate, they are diabolical.

The spirit of offense is often present. If they have been hurt they need to control every situation to ensure this never reoccurs. The spirit of rejection is often present. They need to control every situation and person to ensure they are never rejected again. They will leave or quit before rejection takes place. They will abandon you before you abandon them. The pain of rejection is so strong and this will never happen to me again so I must be in total control. God has no say or place. Here are a few specific examples:

MENTAL MANIPULATION

The enemy rules and reigns in the minds of man. Your mind is a battleground

The enemy manipulates your thoughts

This person plays mind games with themselves and others They release words in the womb of your mind. Your mind is a birthing place. They are aware of this. They purposefully speak their thoughts with the hope of them being planted into your mind. (Satan spoke and manipulated Eve's thoughts and her previous understanding of God's words If they enemy can get into your mind, he can gain control your life, thoughts, and actions

Infirmities can be mental- Something is always wrong; hypochondriac

Women can believe they are pregnant when they are not, and vice versa

EMOTIONAL MANIPULATION

Focus is on your feelings

Moved by your feelings and not by God

Your feelings take precedence over your decisions; not God

(This is how I *feel*. They made me *feel* this way. You don't understand how this makes me *feel*. I don't *feel* like doing this or that)

They refuse to listen to God or anyone else if they don't feel happy or excited

Every action is predicated on how they feel about it
Never right or wrong; feelings are all that matters

You must have an ability and strength to remove your feelings from the equation and adhere to the word of God. This can be extremely difficult for people in the body of Christ.

You cannot serve God and your feelings

Emotions make good company, but not good leaders in any area (households, jobs, church, corporations)

When emotions are high it is hard to handle crisis, children, spouses, etc.

You have tendencies to shut down and shut people out; your world and everything in it stops

When emotional, you are susceptible to make wrong decisions

Never make major decisions when you are emotional; refuse to be pressured or rushed into making a major decision. Stop, gather your emotions, and give yourself time to think and process (Jobs, spouses, marriages, divorces, death, birth, business opportunities)

People who emotionally manipulate force you to respond in a hurry. (We need to talk now; this can't wait; this is too important we must decide now.)

They can't let you have time to think, or get advice for fear you may decide in your favor and not theirs.

They make you believe you will miss out, or that consequences will be dire if you wait.

These are key weapons in the spirit of Manipulation and Control:

INTIMIDATION

They will intimidate you into getting their way

The word timid is inside of the word intimidation

Makes you feel like a prisoner

Invokes fear by mental force (If you don't comply I'll leave; if you tell I'll get you)

My way or the highway

DOMINATION

Attempts to influence your actions

This is what I want you to do; or this is what I don't want you to do

They dominate all aspects of your life

FAULT FINDING

Everything is wrong; nothing is ever right

They will say, "I'm only sharing my thoughts or my feelings" "Never-mind, I won't share anymore because you get offended"

This is an attempt to control your actions

Finds fault with you because they are not satisfied with

themselves

CONDEMNATION

They goal is the break you down to submit.

You are condemned so you finally submit

You walk on eggshells; you begin to practice avoidance;

You don't want to upset them; you decline to talk

THE BLAME GAME

Uses reverse psychology

Someone else is always to blame

They never take responsibility
The are never ever at fault; it is always someone else no matter what

Another person or situation always caused it; never them
Someone made them do this or that

Minimizes everything; turn mountains into molehills, trivialize the nature of a wrongdoing on their part, (It's not that deep; that's not what I meant; it's not that serious) Now you don't focus on their behavior

There's no opportunity to discuss their wrongdoing or error; it's minimized

Diverts your attention away from them (Let's talk about someone else)

Something is in you that attracts this spirit to you!

LYING

This is easy for them

They will stop at nothing to get their way so they will say whatever is needed

You get *their* truth, not the real or complete truth

Lie with Omission- leaves out key or important information Only tells part of the truth;

EXAGGERATION

Always exaggerates; The truth is present, but you add more (3 people gave their lives to the Lord; but they tell the story, "Yes! 10 or 11 people gave their lives to the Lord today!)

Leads to deeper lies

DISTORTION

Gives distorted versions of the truth

Never can remember the entire thing (I can't remember everything about this or that; I forgot) They don't want to disclose the information you are asking about

RATIONALIZATION

Excuses and Justifications

This is huge in the body of Christ

They have an ability to convince you that they are justified in their actions

They excuse their behaviors

You have no right to confront them; no right to speak to them in a particular manner

You have absolutely no right to address them in regards to that matter

They have all of the rights (Who are you to speak to me like that?)

They have a reason for what they did

I am justified in my actions

You must admit and repent for your actions; not excuse or justify them

EVASION

Uses vagueness to avoid being caught

They ramble

They begin to discuss irrelevant topics; addresses everything else but the question

Answer your question with a question (Why are you doing this? Why are you doing this? What do you mean? What do you *mean* what do I mean?)

This is a deliberate form of manipulation used to confuse you

They make you believe you have the issue and not them

You begin to question your validity and your own mind

SEDUCTION

Praises you with flattery; you now trust them

Very supportive

Targets and exploits emotionally needy people

Use your emotional state to charm their way in

They recognize your needs and vulnerabilities; they prey on this

They know you require approval (Tell you everything you want to hear)

They appear to be very attentive to your needs (If the last person failed to do it, they most certainly will)

They melt your resistance

You give up your loyalty, your confidence to them; you are open to them and share your deep thoughts; now they know what to use to gain access to your life or heart

You fear if they leave, they will tell or exploit your weaknesses

FADING CONFUSION

It never happened

I don't know what you're talking about; I have no clue what you are talking about

Constant amnesia

They play dumb

This causes you confusion

You now question your perception and your sanity

You may even question your spirituality (maybe God didn't say that to me. Maybe I can't hear God's voice)

You step down and relinquish your ability to discern and process the situation

I promise you; I honestly believed I was half way there to crazy. I was convinced that I was an immature and selfish woman. I believed I was acting all kinds of stupid, and not ready for any kind of relationship. Now I'm not perfect by a long shot, and I am open to admitting my weaknesses. I always do. Dorian knew this from the beginning. I've never hidden anything from him. I made it crystal clear to Dorian that I am aware of my anger issues and have put strategies in place to manage them. Today, I understand complete deliverance must happen. *Forget management; it can no longer exist! Not in me, and not in Dorian!*

I expressed to Dorian that when frustrated, it's best for me, and everyone else, that I walk away or take a drive in the car. Exercise is also beneficial to my mood as well as my waistline. But if I took a walk, or a drive, or even attempted to exercise without him, I was selfish because it took time away from us.

Every person walking the face of this earth has an area, or multiple areas of deficiencies that, if neglected, become hindrances to our lives. Dorian lives his life as if he has none. I genuinely began to feel sorry for him.

For the duration of my sabbatical I continued to pray for my marriage to be restored and renewed, but I earnestly prayed for Dorian even more. I prayed for God to deliver him from the spirit of rejection, pride, and every other spirit attached to him.

With such an abundance of pride, Dorian would never

receive this as truth; at least not from me. Lord touch him, and then change his heart. Not for me, but for your glory.

By my estimation, since Dorian was convinced that I was the spouse who was in error, I was the spouse who needed to make amends. Dorian had been chastising me profusely, constantly correcting me, and belittlement was becoming the norm. I took it all; every bit of it. I had revisited the Love Dare book and dutifully complied with the dares to the best of my physical ability. Dorian basically rejected any attempts of mine to see, or spend time with him. He knew he held all of the cards and he *loved* it! He believed he was making me pay for what I had done; not knowing how the health of my peace and my mind were being restored, and reaching to an even greater depth in God.

Dorian changed the subject anytime I mentioned 'The Text.' He shifted all conversations back to 'The Gun'. He had the audacity to refuse to address Portia or *any* relating topics concerning her. I had repeatedly asked if we could talk face-to-face, instead of on the phone or via text; he declined. I requested sex; he denied. I inquired about my money for the wedding. He was now working, but his memory of our financial agreement was slowly fading; no deposits. My current responses and reactions to his domineering behavior had changed. Dorian noticed the transformation in behavior. I think he was concerned that his bag of tricks was no longer effective. Dorian decided we meet could meet for dinner.

Forcing myself to hold in the new information I had acquired was a challenge. I engulfed myself into anything I could locate on the topic of manipulation. I wanted him to know that I *knew* what he'd been doing to me the entire time. But self-control was my portion. Red Lobster was our destination. Yes, the same Red Lobster he drove through the snow for me so many months ago. I wished I knew about the spirit of manipulation then. Time could have been saved, and hearts could have been spared.

I brought my notebook with me, and I was ready! I was equipped to respond because I recognized what I was dealing with; a spirit! We began to talk and in true Dorian fashion, he wanted me to apologize for hitting him and endangering his life. I bypassed extending another apology, and I began to tell him that he was operating in a spirit of manipulation. Oh baby, you should've seen his face! He was incredibly offended! As I began to read to him my findings, and relate each and every point to an incident between us, he asked where I'd received this information.

"DeeDee what is this? Where did you gather these, these silly notes?" he pompously asked.

He was critical and hesitant to accept information from sources he felt weren't valid or credible. I posed this question to him. "What if I were to tell you that I received this information from your esteemed Bishop? Can you recall our numerous trips to his church's bookstore after a service? Well Dorian, you're aware Bishop has authored several books correct; many of which you *do not* own. And you yourself have constantly informed me, Bishop is a revelatory and prolific teacher; comparable to none in his understandings of God," I replied.

"Bishop has a tendency to go left at times with some of his teachings," he said. "What? Are you now in disagreement with his understanding of the spirit of manipulation? Normally, you compare him to the likes of Paul and St. John concerning his revelations, but now you are in conflict with his findings? Are you okay Dorian? You appear to be getting very upset?" I asked him.

If Dorian were aware of the true source of this information and the fact that it came from a woman, especially a woman he was unfamiliar with, he would turn his haughty nose up and the conversation would have been over. I needed to hear his response believing it was derived from his Bishop. Dorian was holding a glass of water in his hand, and suddenly slammed it down on the table! *Oh shoot!* Water was everywhere! He was infuriated! I was pushing every button and he was losing control; that perfect sense of control he'd always seem to display. The control that he so proudly taught me was his maturity in action; even while under great pressure, self-control was attainable with discipline. No circumstance was above him losing his head. *But he was losing it now!* His eyes became enlarged as he stared at me with such hate!

That spirit was agitated. I know the secrets now. I was witnessing manifestation right before my very eyes! *This was like a movie!*

I did not relent. I reminded him of the moments in his childhood that were not nurtured and how it was impacting his adulthood. He wanted me to stop reading my notes. He asked me to stop. If he could have strangled me in that restaurant he most definitely would have. *This is why I chose to meet in a public place with witnesses.* I spoke to him about deliverance and asked him to submit to receiving help. I would help him. Dorian became even more irate.

I clearly understood his power was being taken away from him; I was now in control. But I didn't want control; I wanted Dorian to be set free. I refused to use this as leverage, or to wallow in bitterness. I spoke the love of God and so much encouragement to him. His eyes became glassy as if he were about to cry, and then, without warning, I watched the other Dorian reappear; the one who was consistently calm, cool, and collected; always reserved, and extremely prideful. *The spirit was back; it had never left.*

He gathered himself together and suggested that I quickly finish my food because it was time for us to leave. He reiterated that our marriage was less than two years old, and divorce was our best option. It was essential to put his mother, and his children first. I asked him to explain to me his earlier revelations from God concerning me. "I thought God told you I was your treasure? I was the woman you were to marry. What happened to that

Dorian? Did God not reveal this to you?" I questioned. Dorian said he heard incorrectly. He stated that he wanted me, and God had *nothing* to do with it.

"So you are telling me just because you liked me, or believed you loved me, that was enough for you? You didn't consult God? You would marry someone just because you wanted to?" I asked.

He said yes. "That's what bothered me so much about you. I remember the day like it was yesterday. You easily proclaimed to me if God told you no in regards to my proposal, you wouldn't have married me. DeeDee you *never* loved me like I loved you!" he angrily responded.

"Of course I loved you Dorian, but if I honestly believed that God said no, I would not have married you! And you should not have married me if God told you no. You can love someone, but that does not qualify him or her to be in covenant with you. It's not just about love Dorian," I stated.

"Obviously not," he said. I am going through with this divorce.

The weeks passed and although I did initiate communication, Dorian was very cold, abrupt, and distant. Dorian also refused to go to counseling with me. He agreed to speak to my pastors alone, but that didn't manifest either. I resolved to pray and fast on my own, seeking the counsel of God for my marriage. I researched prayers specifically for the restoration of marriages. I even found some African prayers, and you know they work! Our homeland warriors know how to pray down heaven, you hear me! Through this entire process I continued to meditate on Scriptures concerning anger, forgiveness, restoration, and love. I did not give up on my marriage, and I quietly lived my life immersed in a familiar place; a place I had not occupied for a very long time.

A place called Peace.

One afternoon while I was taking my lunch break at work, Dorian texted me and said we needed to talk. I was surprised and hopeful that reconciliation was near. I told him that I was free at the moment, but he said he wanted to talk to me when I left work. I asked if we could speak now; I told him that I was on my lunch and had another 30 minutes before my next class. He texted and said that the conversation would take about ten minutes or so. He called me and was very official.

"Hello DeeDee. I called to let you know that the divorce is now final," Dorian coldly informed.

"Okay. Can you send me a copy of the paperwork?" I gently requested.

He stuttered as if he was thrown off guard by my unbothered response, "Yeah, yes okay, I will send it," he replied. "Thank you Dorian. Goodbye." Click.

> *Therefore, behold, I will allure her, and bring her into the wilderness, and speak tenderly to her.* -Hosea 2:14

CHAPTER FOURTEEN

"REVELATIONS"

There has been no communication between Dorian and I since that faithful afternoon. I promised God during my sabbaticals, periods of solitude, and after my intimate times of consecrations and prayers that I would love God regardless. I will continue to serve him, and accept whatever His will was for my life. God knew I was fully submitted unto him and I completely trusted him with the outcome. Although I was praying for the restoration of my marriage, I also prayed for the restoration of DeeDee. I wanted her back, and I wanted her back complete and whole, without another person having to provide *any portion* in order for her existence to surpass amazing. I wanted her dancing in the mirror again. I wanted her joy from singing loudly in a random supermarket to return. I wanted her confidence in the voice of God, her boldness, *and* her spunkiness, the *best part,* minus the anger, back!

I know we get angry, and of course we all get upset. God has these same emotions. Jesus was our example of how emotions and behaviors should be handled, and to what degree they are to be expressed. Growing up in my household, anger was not expressed in a calm and reserved manner. We did not talk it out; we fought it out! We screamed and shouted when angry. We threw anything within our reach, we hit, we cursed, we smacked; We did it all wrong. We actually went beyond anger and I learned while studying and through prayer that anger was not the spirit I battled; it was rage. I needed deliverance just as much as Dorian. Rage entered my life via environment, pain, and disappointments. And now it was my responsibility to ensure just as it entered, it had to now make its exit.

In the year 2015, I buried my dad, the first man I knew. I wanted so much from him, but he could never provide it. I wanted the presence of the man that was physically abusive towards my mother, and emotionally destructive regarding his kids. But he was still my daddy. Regardless of who my dad was and who he was not, I wanted him in my life. I needed him to teach me things. I wanted him to meet my boyfriends at the door, to scare them and fill them with fear so they understood I was covered and protected. I desired for my father, not my mother, to walk me down the aisle and give me away to a man he approved of. And although I have made decisions to marry *three different men*, who in one way or another all encompass some characteristic of my dad, my daddy never walked me down that aisle. He didn't show up to any of my weddings; much less pay for them. He never gave me away. I gave myself away; time and time again.

This time, the only man that I would give myself to completely, was God. And I am sincerely fine with that.

Since my last conversation with Dorian, we have never communicated again. No texts, no phone calls, no letters of closure. Divorce for me is final. There is no need, except if children are involved, to maintain communication. I do not hate Dorian, I have completely forgiven him, and I actually pray for him; often. Mainly by the leading of God, but I do pray. I initially had a problem with God's numerous requests for intercession on his behalf. I figured God had many warriors on the wall so he could request for someone *else* to pray for the man. But when you are a son of God, an absolute sold out son, you do what your father says. God revealed to me that each time I fervently prayed for him was another blow to the enemy. My prayers for him squashed the enemy's plans for bitterness, hate, unforgiveness, and malice to take root in *me!* My prayers for Dorian released me from all the hurt and pain of this experience. I stopped seeing him as my ex-husband, and began viewing him as my brother in Christ. Well, I'm not completely certain *whose* team Dorian actually plays for.

Remember how God reveals the secret things to His prophets???

What is baffling me is how *after* the divorce, I've received more knowledge about this man than when we were dating, or married. God is my best source, but he is not the only source of new information regarding Dorian. Now be clear, I sought out nothing! DeeDee has returned to dancing in mirrors, and singing in supermarkets; remember? I've moved on from Dorian, but for some reason, God has not.

Information about Dorian's past and present continues, even to this day, to find its way to me. It turns out that my eldest cousin Hope and Georgia are good friends. *What you say?* My family had a reunion the summer before our split, and my cousin kept saying that Dorian looked familiar. She recognized his face, but couldn't readily place it. She did not attend our wedding; so this was her first time meeting my husband. Before we left the cookout she realized who he was. She runs a daycare in Pennsylvania that Dorian's daughter attended.

This summer, a few of my cousins came to visit and we got on the topic of relationships and marriage. One of my younger cousins blurted out, "DeeDee you've never said anything, but what in the world happened with you and Dorian? You two seemed like the perfect couple!"

Whenever I was questioned about our break up, I would give everyone the same generic response. "If God wants you to know what happened, He will have to be the one to tell you."

Only my absolute closest friends and serious prayers warriors knew the real situation. I needed them to understand why I took the sabbaticals, and why I required constant prayer for Dorian and I. My cousins sat on the edge of their seats as I shared my experiences. One of my cousins, Beverly was tripping out! She kept repeating, "Oh my God! Oh my God!" All of us looked at her like what? She told us how she would defend Dorian to her sister Hope, her big sister, every time Hope told her to warn me about Dorian! Apparently Georgia would tell my cousin Hope 'all things Dorian'. Georgia was obviously still concerned about Dorian and kept tabs on him. Hope would beg her to tell me, but Beverly thought Georgia was bitter, mad, and lying. Not until she knew Dorian and I were divorced. Beverly then said she didn't want to give me any second hand information. She felt Hope should be the one to tell me because she was receiving information directly from Georgia. Anyway, the last tea Georgia spilled to Hope about Dorian was, "Girl that man is still a lying mess! According to my child, he is back with the same one he was cheating on *me* with!"

This Portia and Dorian combination goes way back! Further than he shared with me. Dorian told me he and Portia met many, many years ago while working together at a hospital. But it was brought to my attention that they actually attended high school together! These two were high school sweethearts! Why lie about how you two met Dorian? I now also know that Portia actually lives in the same town as Dorian; the town where they attended high school together. This explains so much.

Before we were married, we agreed to move to New Jersey. After we were married, about four months in, Dorian started dragging his feet about moving. His home searches changed from Jersey to White Plains. He blamed it on his mother not adjusting well to change, but I know that was a lie, too. *I knew that was crap when he first said it.* It also explains one particular morning that lingered in my head. I couldn't shake it. Dorian is a fast-paced, almost hyper kind of guy. He moves fast like a rabbit! He insisted on going to the local store for me to grab some sausages for breakfast. *I could say something right here but I'm not.* I was cooking and discovered we only had bacon. I changed up the menu, but he insisted that I have whatever I wanted, and if I preferred sausages he would run to the store and get them. Dorian was gone for an hour! His quick runs to the store normally took him fifteen minutes tops. He said the store was crowded today. At 9:00AM Dorian? I knew something was off.

Another bomb that dropped in my lap was that Portia and her children were now once again attending Dorian's church. Dorian practically called this lady a lunatic; remember? The harsh words spoken about her were nothing more than a ploy to distract me from ever learning the truth about their twisted relationship.

There were several pictures floating around on social media months after our divorce. She was introduced to the congregation as his best friend for the last several years. Where was your best friend during our marriage? Why hadn't I met her? I met other women you were friends with, so why not introduce me to your *best* friend? Oh Dorian, this is so sad.

Dorian interviewed for several jobs and for various positions with no luck. He said he would begin searching out hospitals again for employment. He returns home one day after a major interview with a local hospital with the great news that he had been hired! This was the second or third interview and he aced it. His story to me was after he was hired, he had to go meet the head supervisor. Guess who it was y'all. You got it; Portia! So it turns out that work iPhone he pulled out in the car after my daddy's funeral, was the phone he used to communicate with his Boss Lady. She was responsible for him getting the job. *Well Dorian, Can you ask her for a raise so you can give me back your half of my $25,000?*

I have received a resignation letter to review from a former member of his church. No conversations were had, just an inbox asking if the letter was decent and appropriate. I've run into former members, who attend other churches now. *Okay God, so there is an exodus from his church.* I didn't ask and they didn't tell. What are you showing these people God? It has been 'suggested' that this man *possibly* has illegitimate children with this woman, and there is leaked information of her covered-up abortion. And just when you thought you knew it all, there are more skeletons coming out of this 'Man of God's' closet. This particular information was told to me during the actual editing of this book. It amazes me that I have not made one single phone call, or sent anyone a text in an attempt to find out anything concerning this man, but God continues to reveal the secrets of his life to me. What Dorian refused to honestly share with me, God is sharing for him.

Apparently many years ago Dorian's parents lost their home to financial hardship. Dorian always spoke of his childhood home and how much he loved it. Well, Portia purchased that home and moved in to it many years ago. (So she was living around the corner from us during the entire time of our marriage.) And lastly, against his mother's wishes, he finally made an honest woman out of Portia because the two are now one!

I asked God why I needed to know all of this scandal surrounding him? He reminded me that Dorian's mother and father fought against him when he took over the church. Dorian told me his parents tried to turn the church against him. Wait a minute. The average parent usually *wants* their child to follow in their footsteps, and most definitely most parents in the church. This is the same mother that Dorian greatly admired for her accurate levels of discernment. Why did they fight him? What do they know that we don't? This it way too much God! I will continue to pray for him and his wife as you lead,, but please stop sending me his business. That's between you two. I'm out of it now! God said to me, "There is more to come; keep praying."

> *God will judge us for everything we do, including every secret thing, whether good or bad.- Ecclesiastes 12:14*

CHAPTER FIFTEEN

"LESSONS"

GOD'S VOICE TRUMPS ALL! Period. When the marriage first ended, I was in a continuous state of confusion. "I thought God said yes concerning Dorian! Was Dorian the counterfeit, or did I abort the promise? My pastor is a true prophet of God! He saw his children and aspects of their personalities as they were developing in their mother's womb; Why didn't he see this? All of these spiritual and anointed vessels of God confirmed Dorian's character; Can they all be blind? Is his entire church blind? How could you allow me to marry him? How is he allowed to breathe your air while perpetuating such a fraud? Who do I tell? Does it even matter if I tell? Who is going to believe me? His Bishop won't believe me. No one believed Georgia! She was telling the truth!"

I went on for months badgering God with these questions. When I was ready to hear the truth, God answered:

"Little girl, you hate liars just like I do. I showed you he was a liar when he was in that parking lot with Portia. You know my word and my expectations. When he was trying to persuade you to act contrary to my word (and at times he was successful), I was revealing him to you. You let him convince you to sin against my word. You know better! I didn't change my standards; you lowered yours. You allowed him to cross boundaries you had in place. Stop it with "What about all these other people?" I told you to trust no man over me! And as for your pastor, he is my prophet; he is not me! I allow you all to prophesy in part. The same way I open the ears and eyes of man; I close them as I desire. You trusted his ear over your own. I told you who you were! BELIEVE ME!

YOU ARE RESPONSIBLE FOR YOUR ACTIONS. I take full responsibility for my marriage to Dorian. I allowed other people's opinions and perspectives to sway my own views and standards. I trusted their voice over God's. I allowed confusion and anxiety to fuel my decisions. I neglected to practice patience, and to simply wait on God. I was afraid to walk away for fear of missing out. I was lectured that most first ladies endure similar situations and you are not unique or special. It happens to the best of them. You'll get over it.

At the time of my meeting Dorian, and years before that, I did not fully comprehend my own value. I was ignorant concerning the enemy's devices. I, like many other women in God, believed that if he had a relationship with God, and I had a relationship with God, everything would be okay; regardless of the issues. I was not oblivious or naive to the reality that trials and situations would arise between us. My thought process was, if the Word of God is our mandate, our guide, and our directive, and because we have both committed 100% to this truth, we could make it through anything! Right? Right.

But the problem here is that one of us was committed to God, and the other was committed to something else. You can only control yourself. Be responsible for you.

IT'S EASY TO SPOT A FAKE; READ THE WORD.

"Everyone who sins is breaking God's law, for all sin is contrary to the law of God. And you know that Jesus came to take away our sins, and there is no sin in him. Anyone *who continues* to live in him will not sin, but anyone who *keeps on sinning* does not know him or understand who he is. Dear children, don't let anyone deceive you about this: when people do what is right, it shows that they are righteous, even as Christ is righteous. But when people *keep on sinning,* it shows that they belong to the devil, who had been sinning since the beginning. But the Son of God came to destroy the works of the devil. Those who have been born into God's family do not *make a practice of sinning,* because God's life is in them. So they can't *keep on sinning,* because they are children of God. So now we can tell who <u>are children of God</u> and who are children of the devil. Anyone who does not live righteously and does not love other believers, does not belong to God. 1John 3:4-10 (NLT) **emphasis added.**

HAVE PATIENCE! If you feel like you are being rushed, then 9 times out of 10 you are, so stand firm in your decision to wait. Never allow anyone to back you up against a wall or pressure you to make a decision. If the pace you have established for yourself is too slow for someone else, allow him or her to move ahead without you. Stop thinking you will miss out. If it's God will, it shall manifest. Your understanding should be if they move on without *you, they* would miss out on the awesomeness of YOU! And that's okay too.

Allow God to lead you and direct every step of your blessed life. You actually may not be ready to go at their speed, or function on their level right now; that is fine. God might not be finished processing you. This is not only advice for relationships, but business, and life as well. Many times, we witness others successfully operating in areas of our interest, so we attempt to jump from our current situation, to their present one. They've mastered the process and steps of 1-10, and because their 10 looks awesome, you attempt to jump from your 4 to their 10. You will never be able to maintain their 10. Your bricks of 5-9 were never laid, and now you are missing pivotal steps for a foundation that you never took the proper time to lay. Your structure will collapse.

YOUR TIME WILL COME. Two years after everything went down, as I've already stated in the beginning of this book, the Lord told me to tell my story. He literally woke me up in the middle of the night, and told me to write this book. He titled this narrative himself! I was actually working on a different book at the time, but He said this book was needed in the earth now. This is what I was told. "I needed you to be quiet for the last couple of years because it was necessary for you to process everything. I needed to restore you. I had to ensure that bitterness had not taken root, and I did not want you to speak out of anger, but out of truth. Now, you have to go help my people. Many believe when you say "God" or if you mention you attend "church", this equals a person's purity and commitment to me. It does not! Remind them of my word! Not everyone who calls out to me Lord, Lord will enter the Kingdom of heaven! You will know them by their fruit; by how the act and behave.

Too many women have been in your situation and are still living in your situation. They marry men who profess to know me, but they do not! Many men and women have not been delivered in areas that would allow them to be Godly spouses. There are demonic spirits in the church! Train them to identify those spirits, and how to recognize the voice of The Holy Spirit. I need you to warn my daughters who are naïve in the same ways you were. I need you to help restore my daughters. Minister to them. You cannot be quiet! I made you a watchman. I called you to be a prophet to the nations; not a prophet to yourself! You can't keep my knowledge for yourself! My people are perishing because they do not know. Do not fear; do not be scared of their faces! Their opinions about you don't matter. I matter. You are my instrument. Go and tell your story."

TRUST GOD IN EVERY SITUATION. As difficult as most of this story has been to write, it was even more challenging recalling who *I* was at the time; how naïve and insecure I could be during those short years with Dorian. Recalling some of the moments of this 'tell-all' of my business and 'help-all' of your people manuscript, has forced me to relive some of the most horrible moments of my life. Many twenty-four hour days felt like eternity. God, will the day ever arrive when pain doesn't greet me in the morning, and tuck me into bed at night?

However, writing this book has also empowered me to stand firm in my truth without any regret, or fear of opinions. My prayer for you is that my story reminds you to cultivate an incredible relationship with God; one that can only be achieved with intimacy. I pray for the value you place on yourself to exceed the most precious diamonds and gems in this world.

The hell that I endured will be used to help as many women that are available to receive it. Although this experience nearly cost me my sanity, peace of mind, and my uncanny ability to rise above the ashes, I have gained priceless knowledge, and I assure you that my confidence in God's word and in His voice, is unshakeable. My mistakes, my transparency, my heart, my mind, my innocence, my guilt, my salvation, and my sins are now resting in the palms of your hands. I ask that you please handle them with care. Pass them along to another broken heart. Learn from the lessons I have already lived and do not repeat them. You may not survive; I almost didn't.

While ministering to many different women on several different occasions, I saw the overwhelming necessity of telling this story. I knew that one day God was going to allow me to finally speak. Today is that day. Thank you for listening.

Love,
DeeDee

In the morning on January 8, 2018, I clicked on a post from Facebook sharing Oprah Winfrey's acceptance speech for receiving the Cecil B. Demille award. Her eloquent and powerful speech was a summation of my heart's cry.

Excerpts from Oprah Winfrey's Golden Globes 2017 Acceptance Speech

"What I know for sure, is that speaking your truth is the most powerful tool we all have. And I'm especially proud and inspired by all the women who have felt strong enough, and empowered enough to speak up and share their personal stories."

"Justice wasn't an option in the era of Jim Crow. The men who tried to destroy her, (Recy Taylor) were, never persecuted. She lived, as we all have lived, too many years in a culture broken by brutally powerful men. For too long women have not been heard or believed, if they dared to speak their truth to the power of those men. But their time is up."

"In my career, what I've always tried my best to do, whether on television or through film, is to say something; about how men and women really behave. To say how we experience shame, how we love, and how we rage, how we fail, how we retreat, persevere, and how…we… overcome. I've interviewed and portrayed people who've withstood some of the ugliest things life can throw at you, but the one quality, all of them seem to share, is an ability to maintain hope for a brighter morning; Even during our darkest nights.

"So I want all the girls, watching here and now to know, that a NEW DAY IS ON THE HORIZON! And when that new day, finally dawns.... it will be because of a lot of magnificent women, many of whom are right here in this room tonight, and some pretty phenomenal men, fighting hard to make sure that they become the leaders who take us to the time when nobody has to ever say, ME TOO, again.

(Insert my SCREAM- YESSSSSSSSSS, YES GOD!!!!!)

ACKNOWLEDGEMENTS

The Father, The Son, and The Holy Spirit have truly given me the strength and boldness to pen such a transparent and paramount story. Thank you Lord God for your Grace upon my life, and the courage to stand in my truth. I remain in constant awe of you! Please allow me to forever remain in your presence and perpetually experience your glory.

Mommy, you are my Ultimate Inspiration! My tenacity, my fire, my spirit of determination all come as a result of growing up and watching you conquer every obstacle placed before you. You are my real-life Wonder Woman! Thank you for every sacrifice given, each lesson taught, and for all the love a mother could give. I promise to take care of you and to always honor you. I love you to life!

To the absolute, most incredible body of believers on this planet, **NEW LIFE NOW CHURCH!!!** Thank you for rocking with me for the last eight years! Your continuous prayers, love, support, and spiritual warfare, on my behalf has not been in vain. The first baby is here!!! Let's continue to advance God's agenda collectively and individually as we all pursue the mandates of God for our lives. I am forever in His service for you all.

Joyce Francis Berry My life could not exist without our Lord and savior, but it certainly would be more difficult to navigate if you were not apart of it. You have been supporting me, pushing me, aggravating me, laughing and crying with me for over 30 years; and we are STILL so fly! LOL! You've helped me to survive the most unbearable moments of my life and I am forever grateful for your role as my best friend, my confidant, and my 'Peter'.

Pamela Long We bravely walked nearly parallel paths during simultaneous times of our lives. You understood the depths of my pain because you were experiencing an agony of the same magnitude. I thank God for allowing us to lean on one another, and giving us the strength to hold each other up from then, until now. You are truly my sister from another mother. Thank you for being my prayer partner, spiritual warrior, and a calm in the storm.

Godzchild Inc. Publishing House Shaun Saunders you have been a Godsend to my life beginning over five years ago when a 5am prayer call shifted a particular course in my life. Thank you and Godzchild Inc. for providing me with such excellence, top-notch professionalism, and absolute clear direction with the publication of my first book! I will always remember how you embraced this project as if it were your very own. I love you and Ana dearly!

To the voices crying out in the wilderness; to those prophetic vessels of honor; some of whom I personally know, and others whom I do not. Your steady push and constant reminders to WRITE THE BOOK, TELL YOUR STORY, & FINISH THE BOOK were divinely inspired and it coached me from the sidelines during times when life was most difficult. **Sophia Ruffin, Apostle John Eckhardt, Zaire Codrington, Shaun Saunders, and Charla Saunders;** THANK YOU!!!